In Memoriam
Jean-Florian, great pencil and paintbrush wizard...

Credits

AUTHOR
Antoine Bauza

ADDITIONAL MATERIAL
Patrick Kapera, Amanda Valentine,
and Clark Valentine

ILLUSTRATOR
Arnü West

COLORIST
Albertine Ralenti

LAYOUT
Michal E. Cross, Thomas Kohler

EDITORS
Alex Flagg, Patrick Kapera, and Amanda Valentine

DEVELOPMENT
Amanda Valentine

TRANSLATORS
Franck Florentin and Amanda Valentine

THANKS (FRENCH EDITION)
To lil' Sorcerer Paul-Henri "Pitche" Verheve for his tireless and keen guidance, and his continued support

To lil' Mage David, for his help building Coinworld

To lil' Mage Manu, for his earnest support

To my beloved lil' Sorcerer Albertine for... everything!

To all the authors who have written and told tales of magic through the ages

To Aurélia, whose name mysteriously disappeared from the first French release, and to Sethmes for our many conversations about Yaks!

To Grümph for the Shivers and the Moon Herb

THANKS (ENGLISH EDITION)
To Amanda's own Little Wizards, Mary Rose and Thad, for the playtesting, inspiration, and brainstorming

To Clark for his unending support in so very many different ways

Contents

A Lil' Word from the Author, Antoine Bauza

You just started reading *Little Wizards*, a game book intended for people who love marvelous and magical stories.

The Tales in this book are special because they will be told and lived by you, the player.
So indulge your imagination and let Coinworld's magic make you laugh and dream.

"Childhood is the most marvelous of all experiences."
~ Melissa, Dean of Sorcerers

"Magic is the most marvelous of all adventures."
~ Balivern, High Mage of BentBack

A Lil' Word from the Developer, Amanda Valentine

To the parents, older siblings, cool aunts & uncles, game club sponsors, and others who might be looking to play this game with the kids in their lives…

Little Wizards is intended as an introduction to roleplaying games for kids ages 6 to 10 or so. It's also full of advice for running games for young players, who don't always follow the same conventions we've learned in our years of gaming.

Both players and the Narrator (the GM role) are addressed in the book, and I hope your kids will enjoy looking through it. However, while the game is geared for younger children to play, I've assumed that the game will be narrated by either an adult or an older kid with some experience playing roleplaying games. Then, once they've played *Little Wizards* a few times, young players may be ready to step into the role of Narrator.

Playtesting *Little Wizards* with my kids was my first experience as a GM. Part of my goal with this game is to provide guidance and advice for new GMs — whether you're running a game for the first time or just running a game for kids for the first time.

I hope *Little Wizards* will be a fun introduction to the wonderful world of playing and running roleplaying games.

Introduction

What is a Little Wizards Tale?

Little Wizards is a game of cooperative storytelling around a table (or around a fireplace during winter, or — why not? — around a pool during summer). It's a game without winners and, more importantly, without losers. You and your friends work together to create characters in an imaginary world and tell awesome stories about them. Everyone wins when the stories are fun.

In *Little Wizards*, you imagine a character, with her qualities and flaws, and you take her through extraordinary adventures. It's a game of imagination and interpretation, where you assume a role — a little like in a movie or a play.

Let's use the example of *Peter Pan*. The main characters include Peter Pan, Wendy, Tinker Bell, and Captain Hook. The world of *Peter Pan* is Neverland, with its magic, Lost Boys, and pirates.

Now imagine you can take the role of one of the characters in the adventure. How would the story be different if Peter didn't ignore Tinker Bell after Wendy came to Neverland? What if Michael or John didn't want to go back home with Wendy? What if Wendy acted a bit more like the Lost Boys and a bit less like their mother? This is how things happen in *Little Wizards*: you put yourself in the shoes of an imaginary character — a lil' Wizard — and *you* decide how his story unfolds!

A *Little Wizards* **Tale** is an adventure story that you and your friends tell as part of the game. We provide some to get you started (*see pages 70, 90, and 109*), but of course you can make up your own! The stories all take place in **Coinworld** — a strange, poetic, and magical location, hidden amidst the stars.

In a *Little Wizards* Tale, the players tell the story together. Each of you plays a Wizard — either a Sorcerer or a Mage — who's an extraordinary girl or boy, gifted with magical powers. One player, called the Narrator, guides the story and plays the role of all the other characters. As a player, you also get to write some of the story; in *Little Wizards*, everyone is a bit of a Narrator!

(see pages 70, 90, and 109)

Note to the Narrator

Throughout the book, you'll find notes like this one, offering options, advice, and suggestions to help you in the role of the Narrator.

The Narrator has a number of responsibilities, including:

- **Acting as a director:** establishing the setting, putting events into action, and incorporating the actions of the characters played by the players, as well as roleplaying the other characters himself. We'll talk about these responsibilities in more detail in The Narrator, starting on page 63.

- **Acting as a referee:** knowing and applying the rules in a fair and fun way. For example, when two characters race, the Narrator has final say on who wins (the guidelines in Basic Rules on page 39 will help him decide).

We offer lots of advice for narrating *Little Wizards* Tales later in this book.

What's in This Book?

- An **introduction** explaining the various elements of *Little Wizards* and how to play

- An **overview** of Coinworld, where Tales take place

- **Rules** for creating your character and taking part in Tales

- **Guidelines** to help the Narrator fulfill her role

- Three **Tales** ready for you to play, and more details about the Steppes and Shivers Archipelagos

What Do We Need to Play?

- **Players:** there's no game without players, of course! *Little Wizards* is designed for least two players in addition to the Narrator, but it works with just one player and a Narrator. There's no real upper limit, but four players is a good number.

- **A Narrator:** she's a special player. She's in charge of telling the story that happens around the other players' characters. The Narrator knows all the places and all the characters in the world, and most importantly, all the Tale's secrets.

- **A Little Wizards Tale:** this is a story especially written to be told and played by several players. There are three in this book, ready for you to play.

- **A few accessories:** not much — a few pencils, two 6-sided dice (the cube-shaped ones you find in many board games), and a few photocopies of the character sheet at the end of this book. You may also want small tokens for Lil' Points (*see page 57*), and maybe a few index cards for keeping notes.

- **Some time:** a game can last from one to three hours, depending on the Tale. You can cut a Tale into several chapters and play them over several games, each whatever length you like.

- **Imagination!** The one thing that no game of *Little Wizards* can do without is you and your ideas. Get ready to think up some of your best stories because that's what this game is all about!

Coinworld

The characters of *Little Wizards* live in your imaginations, but they also inhabit their own world, called **Coinworld**. Here's a small tour of its marvels.

This World Isn't Really Like Any Other

Imagine you go for a walk though the infinite universe, following a trail of stars. You see a great number of planets along the way, of all sizes and colors. Some have rings, others hide beneath a thick gas veil. All of them reveal their beautiful roundness to the rays of the neighboring suns...

Well, not all of them! If you keep walking past a large moon with a blue gleam, and if you take time to loiter among the clusters of stars, you'll find this small planet that managed to escape the normal laws of astronomy.

This small, circular, flat world is hidden away, nestled in a bed of shiny stars. It's like a tiny coin deep in the galaxy's pocket, and as your curiosity draws you a little closer you discover a world full of life, magic, and mystery. It's a unique place with rules all its own. It's a place called... **Coinworld**.

As you may have already guessed, this place is like a coin, which by definition has two faces. Coinworld's first face is called **Heads** and the second is **Tails**.

Heads...

Let's first take a look at Heads.

Dressed with a deep blue ocean, it's an enchanting place with soothing charm. Its islands hide magnificent forests that give shelter to many animals. Creatures run among the tree trunks, fly through their branches, and nestle in their roots. Mountains of all ages drowse peacefully, kept cool by their springs and rivers. Great plains are caressed by fragrant winds. Deserts are hot, but not too hot, and glaciers are cold, but not too cold.

People native to Heads admire, cherish, and preserve their natural environment. They've built civilizations that are respectful of the world they inherited and they live in harmony with nature.

The inhabited lands of Heads consist of five small groups of islands: the Keys Archipelago in the center, the Smiles Archipelago to the west, the Steppes Archipelago to the north, the Whispers Archipelago to the east, and the Wilds Archipelago to the south.

...and Tails

Let's leave Heads' mostly peaceful shores to explore the other side of the coin, Tails. Here the ocean is just as big but it has an orange tint and the sky is gloomier, making it almost frightening. The ground is darker, and the tree leaves are a deep green. Winds are cold and often strong, and the mountains have sharp, knifelike peaks. The plants and animals here are strange and surprising.

None of this prevented civilizations from settling down near the reefs or beside the windswept moors. The people of Tails have learned to embrace their surroundings, and many of them thrive here. They harness the winds and torrential rains as sources of power, and they often celebrate the many mysteries and creepy things that live alongside them. Life on Tails is just as good as it is on Heads — at least, for those who've grown up in its strange and eerie atmosphere.

Just like on Heads, the inhabited lands of Tails are divided into five small groups of islands: the Bones Archipelago in the center, the Storms Archipelago to the west, the Shivers Archipelago to the north, the Screams Archipelago to the east, and the Wyrds Archipelago to the south.

Two Sides of the Same Coin

Coinworld's two sides have a lot in common — more than you'd expect at first glance. Some Sorcerer legends and a few old Mage books suggest that living things from both faces are closely connected, that every being on Heads has an alter ego on Tails. And in some ways it does seem like each archipelago might have a mirror on the opposite side of the coin.

How are the two faces linked? Can one exist without the other? No one knows for sure.

One thing we do know is that there's no easy way to go from one face to the other. You need magic to travel from Heads to Tails, and from Tails to Heads. Experienced magic users, like older Sorcerers and Mages, can change sides pretty easily, and some magic items make that kind of travel possible. There are also rumors of a few magical locations that can be used as gates between the two sides.

Coinworld is, overall, a happy and peaceful place. There's no famine or plague; there have been no wars in modern memory. For the most part, the people of this small world understand that the things they do affect the other people on their little planet. They're generally happy to help each other out.

Not Quite the Modern World

Technology on Coinworld isn't very widespread, and even the most advanced archipelagos are a bit behind our world's — for instance, the most "modern" homes on Coinworld are just starting to get electrical appliances (ovens, refrigerators, washing machines, and so on). In the cities, gas heating is gradually replacing oil stoves and fireplaces. Running water is common in urban areas, although wells and creeks still supply water in the countryside. Some towns are setting up water treatment plants to protect their environment.

When people want to communicate with others who are far away, letters are the most common method. Mail can be slow, but the letters almost always arrive to the right place and person. Postal carriers use whatever means of transportation makes sense — planes, railways, and boats. Phones are still new to Coinworld and are found mostly in cities; people living elsewhere often have to use the one community phone, usually located at the post office. Phone calls are made through operators — people who connect the caller to the person they're calling.

Bicycles are commonly ridden to work and school, and for fun. Cars are a new invention, found mainly on the Smiles Archipelago. Trains travel between cities and boats travel between archipelagos. Planes are small, flown mostly by the postal services and daring adventurers.

Magic and Sorcery

Two strange and wonderful phenomena coexist on this strange and wonderful planet: **Sorcery** and **Magic**.

Sorcery is inherited from parent to child. Its purpose has always been to serve nature and the people of Coinworld. Sorcerers have a special link to Coinworld, and access to numerous Powers: they use **Spellcasting**, **Alchemy**, and **Divination** to help others, with the guidance of their **Elders**, the oldest and most respected Sorcerers.

Pupils learn Magic from masters in fantastical schools with unusual names. Mages record their secrets in spell books and use **Spellcasting**, **Conjuring**, and **Shapechanging** under the attentive watch of the **Sages**, the wisest and most powerful Mages.

Like the lil' Wizard you'll play, most Mages and Sorcerers live among the other people of Coinworld, helping them solve problems. A few retire from the cities, living alone like hermits in remote locations. Other less commendable individuals choose a selfish path, using Magic and Sorcery for their own profit. These scoundrels make things difficult on Coinworld, and are frequent adversaries for your *Little Wizards* heroes!

A Lil' Bit About the Archipelagos

So what will a Wizard find if she travels to the different archipelagos? Let's take a closer look at each one.

Heads: The Keys Archipelago

A place for everything, and everything in its place! So say many who live on the Keys Archipelago, the central islands on Heads. Everything is on schedule, everything is tidy and neat and orderly, and the rules keep it that way. *Oh, the rules.* So many rules... Rules about big things like stealing and hurting people. Rules about little things like the proper way to speak and the proper clothes to wear. Keys is home to some of the best detectives and sleuths on Coinworld, and these stalwart searchers are always on the case to find anyone breaking the rules (mostly the big ones) so they can be brought to justice.

The people of Keys have a great love of learning; Keys is home to some of Coinworld's best libraries, museums, and schools (magic and otherwise). Artifacts from all over the world can be found in these museums for the curious to view, and breathtakingly beautiful creatures of all kinds are kept in neighboring zoos and menageries. Wise and learned scholars flock to Keys to teach and learn about these items and exotic beings.

By the rules, some places on Keys are off-limits to all but a select few. Rumors abound of what might be found in these places... Are there old mansions housing great libraries of dangerous magic? Ancient forests where herds of dragons roam? Secret laboratories where mad scientists build amazing and terrible inventions? A Wizard could spend her whole life solving these mysteries...

Heads: The Smiles Archipelago

The Smiles Archipelago is a well established, well ordered land. The people enjoy a comfortable lifestyle, with new technology — telephones, refrigerators, and automobiles make things easier for them every day. Some people say this also makes them a bit stuffy and boring, leaning on devices to solve their problems rather than risk an adventure to figure it out for themselves.

Smiles is also home to countless curious and playful faeries. Most of these beings keep to themselves in the forests and mountains, but some venture down into the peoples' lands. The faeries have decided it's their job to keep the peoples' lives from getting too boring, and they make mischief of all kinds. Usually it's harmless fun, but sometimes it's handy to have a lil' Wizard around to keep things from getting too out of control.

Heads: The Steppes Archipelago

The towering Malayak Mountains are visible to those approaching the Steppes Archipelago long before they lay eyes on the shoreline. These cloud-wrapped mountains dominate the islands, and hold the frigid north winds at bay.

Some fishing villages are nestled on the southern shore but most people are nomadic herders, following the huge groups of yaks that wander the mountain passes and high meadows beyond the first line of peaks. Steppish herders are a hardy, no-nonsense people carving out good lives in a harsh environment. They value stories, history, music, and games — all wonderful things to pass the time during the long summer afternoons and deep winter nights of the far north.

Even so, in some winters the snows pile too deep, and both people and yaks get lost. Villages are cut off and require assistance. More than one explorer has had an all-too-close call deep in the snowy mountains of the Steppes.

For more details about the Steppes Archipelago, see page 83. "Lost in Malayak" on page 90 is a Tale you can play, set in this island chain.

Heads: The Whispers Archipelago

Many historians think the Whispers Archipelago is the most ancient land on Coinworld. Records go back a dozen centuries here, with every family and village meticulously recording every important event: births, deaths, marriages, jobs, and all sorts of happy and sad occasions are put down in history books. Everyone is taught the details of their family history, the triumphs and the tragedies. People often struggle to live up to the legacies of their ancestors here — which, despite meticulous records, are often exaggerated anyway! Some people even claim they can speak with their ancestors using powerful magic, and maybe they really can.

This cultural drive to record and remember everything has a down side: grudges can linger, as wrongs and slights — both real and imagined — fester and grow over the years. Traveling Wizards are often called upon to mediate between bickering inhabitants of Whispers, before someone's feelings are hurt.

Heads: The Wilds Archipelago

The Wilds Archipelago is, not surprisingly, the least populated and least developed of the lands on Heads. It's an intensely magical place, and its mostly unmapped wilderness is home to countless magical creatures and crumbling stone ruins — castles and temples the forest is slowly reclaiming. Nobody knows who built these structures, or what happened to those who lived here.

The people of Wilds are friendly and practical. They have learned to respect the great power nature wields here, and they think of themselves as guests of the forests and hills, not owners of them. Some of the most powerful nature Sorcerers in Coinworld hail from Wilds, but even they usually stay out of the forest ruins, preferring to let nature retake them.

Because of the strength of nature magic in Wilds, Wizards from all over Coinworld know this is one of the best places to recruit a familiar. It takes more than just showing up and asking for a familiar, though; striking out into the wilds, finding a magical creature, and convincing it to become your companion is an adventure in itself. Every animal is unique, and they're just as picky about their masters as Wizards are about them.

Tails: The Bones Archipelago

Avast, ye sailors and scallywags! The Bones Archipelago at the center of Tails is home to people the sea couldn't find a respectable home for — pirates, buccaneers, and other unsavory sorts who prefer a life of swashbuckling to that of an upstanding sailor. Many of these people make a lot of money raiding honest ships' crews as they sail around Tails.

A handful of harbors dot these islands, welcoming dozens of ships and their crews of raiders and thieves. There are also those seeking adventure or hoping to escape a bad situation in one of the other archipelagos; Bones is a place where anyone can start over, where people don't judge someone by their past.

Wizards often come to Bones seeking important items and artifacts stolen by pirates. Occasionally, a Wizard decides to take up the pirate's life, and others may follow to convince him of the error of his ways. Either way, Bones is rarely the best place to relax!

Tails: The Storms Archipelago

The people of Storms pride themselves on their strength and toughness, and they refuse to let their islands' punishing environment drive them away. Here the wind and rain are relentless, and the steep mountains push right up to the sea, leaving very little room for the tiny fishing villages that cling to the rocks. Volcanic eruptions sometimes send the natives running for cover and blanket the land in fine ash. Those who make homes here are hardy people indeed.

The limited space for villages and harbors often leads to arguments between the families and tribes of Storms. Wizards are called upon to resolve disputes dating back generations, or to help the people carve out new homes in the unfriendly landscape. The solutions almost always involve reminding everyone to work together.

There are rumors of dragonriders in Storms. Ancient tales speak of fire lizards dwelling in the mountains, which can be tamed by unusually brave and determined adventurers. Each year, a handful of courageous Wizards head out to find these amazing beasts. Most never see a dragon. Some never return at all, though perhaps they live and fly with new companions now.

Tails: The Shivers Archipelago

Shivers isn't a place for the easily startled. It's home to a *very* wide array of people — ordinary humans, but also werewolves, vampires, zombies, and even more exotic and frightening creatures. No one who lives here thinks this is odd in the slightest; creatures like these are accepted as a normal part of Shivers society. In fact, the highest and most respected art form on Shivers is telling scary stories. Maybe it's because everyone is so used to seeing very scary people and things every day, but they seem to love the thrill of a good, spooky tale.

One of the things Wizards most often do on Shivers is deal with visitors to the archipelago who panic at the sight of a werewolf or a vampire and, with the very best intentions, try to "protect" the ordinary folk who live here. (Shivers vampires in particular find this behavior extremely insulting, and can you blame them? Would you react well to someone charging you with a stake?)

For more details about the Shivers Archipelago, see page 101. "The Squeakydoor Manor Mystery" on page 109 is a Tale you can play, set in this island chain.

Tails: The Screams Archipelago

This archipelago is named for the howling wind that blows endlessly through the canyons of its main island, the interior of which is a complete mystery. No explorer has ventured in and returned to tell the tale.

The people of these islands live in villages on the far north and south edges, where the wind is only a distant rumble. In between, the dense jungles and mountains are impenetrably dark and shrouded in deep fog. Some say that titanic creatures from prehistory roam the land there, while others speculate that the source of magic itself is hidden in misty glens unseen for hundreds of years. Some say the ancients — the first people of Coinworld who disappeared long ago — have withdrawn to this place, where they're hidden by the great and magical wind at the center of Screams.

Only the most intrepid Wizards stand a chance of solving this mystery...

Tails: The Wyrds Archipelago

The southern archipelago on Tails is populated mostly by unfriendly and dangerous monsters: goblins, trolls, ogres, and sometimes even malicious magical creatures. A few brave homesteaders from other archipelagos have decided to try to make a home for themselves here, whether because they had no other option or because they relish the challenge. The land is largely wilderness, with vast areas of uncharted forest, desert, and mountains separating these lonely villages and towns. A few bigger towns are defended by armored knights in castles, these brave warriors keeping the monsters away so the rest can eke out a meager living in the Wyrds.

Wizards are always welcomed here, as there are many problems in Wyrds that only those with magic can solve. Many Wizards also visit to explore the wilderness, seeking new wonders in the dangerous forests and among the unusual beasts.

An Enormous Playing Field!

It would be impossible to cover all of Coinworld's charms in this small space. Don't worry — your *Little Wizards* Tales take care of that. We include three in this book, each with new details about your new home: new locations for you to visit, and new animals and characters for you to meet.

The Steppes and Shivers Archipelagos are explored in some detail on pages 83 and 101. We're sure you'll find even more to add to these places, though, and we can't wait to hear about your adventures!

Creating a Wizard

In this chapter you'll find everything you need to create your own lil' Wizard — the person whose story you'll tell during the game. It's all explained, step by step. Just follow the guide!

First, grab a pencil and a copy of the character sheet on page 128. This sheet has spaces for all your decisions about your character and her familiar. This way, you won't forget anything during the game.

What Kind of Wizard are You?

The first and maybe most important choice you make is what sort of Wizard you want to be: either a **lil' Sorcerer** (who is born with Sorcery) or a **lil' Mage** (who learns Magic).

Lil' Sorcerers

FROM PARENT TO CHILD

Every Sorcerer is the child of a Sorcerer. On Coinworld, the gift of Sorcery has been inherited from generation to generation since the dawn of time. Many scholars have researched the question of how this works but no one has settled on a solid theory. Sometimes the gift skips one or several generations but all Sorcerers are sure to find at least one other Sorcerer among their ancestors.

WHAT OTHER PEOPLE THINK OF SORCERERS

In the past, some inhabitants of Coinworld have been suspicious of Sorcerers because of their mysterious powers, but today this feeling has almost completely faded. Sorcerers are welcome in cities, small towns, and rural areas. They're respected and everyone calls upon their powers: men, women, children, animals... and even plants!

Lil' Mages

SCHOOL DAYS

There's no heredity involved in learning Magic, though not everyone has a talent for it. When they're very young, some kids show a knack for it. They can go to one of the many Magic schools of Coinworld, where they study with learned Sages and practice methods of tapping and controlling forces that are well documented and largely understood.

WHAT OTHER PEOPLE THINK OF MAGES

Despite their powers being so well known, Mages are often viewed with suspicion. Magic schools, and their sometimes mischievous students, are frequently blamed for troubles in the communities of Coinworld. Older Mages therefore insist that apprentices help people as often as possible, hoping that if others see how useful Magic can be they'll forget their prejudices. Needless to say, missteps and mishaps are harshly reprimanded.

What Are You Like?

In *Little Wizards*, you play an extraordinary child. The first step is to describe your Wizard. You have a few choices in each category:

+ Make up details on your own.

+ Pick anything you like off a list.

+ Roll some six-sided dice and see what you get.

+ Use some combination of any of those!

Appearance

Describe your lil' Wizard's looks — his size, his build, his hair color, his eye color, the way he dresses, and his signature features (glasses, birthmark, scar, freckles, etc.).

If you already have a good sense of what your lil' Wizard looks like, that's great — you can write down

what you imagine. You can also look at the following lists for inspiration. You might notice that there are some unusual and magical features, such as hair that changes color, a fox's tail, and pointy ears like a cat. Coinworld is a magical place, and sometimes this has a unique influence on those who live there.

If you want help deciding on things that are unusual about your Wizard, roll one of your six-sided dice. The first time you roll, you get a feature — eyes, hair, ears, face, body, or clothes. The second time you roll, you get a specific description about that feature. You can roll as many or as few times as you like. You can reroll or ignore any results you don't want.

These descriptions don't change any of your dice rolls — a monkey's tail won't make it easier for you to climb tall trees or let you hang upside down from your broom, for example — but each of these gives you a way to describe *how* your Wizard climbs a tree or hangs onto his broom, or whatever other actions you think are interesting.

Result 1: A face with...

1	...pointy teeth in your mouth
2	...freckles
3	...an exceptionally pointy nose
4	...face paint
5	...red rosy cheeks
6	...whiskers: like a cat or dog? A walrus?

Result 2: Eyes that...

1	...sparkle. Is it with mischief? Maybe due to your cheery personality?
2	...are dark brown, blue, purple, or another color. Maybe you have dark or colored lashes?
3	...look skeptical, perhaps with one eyebrow always raised
4	...are narrow, perhaps like a cat's eyes
5	...are bright green, blue, violet, or another color
6	...are big and round, maybe like a cartoon character or a puppy

Result 3: Hair that...

1	...changes color every day or maybe at your whim
2	...is wild and unruly
3	...is bright red, green, blue, pink, or another color
4	...isn't there: you're bald
5	...is styled in a mohawk
6	...shows your emotions: droopy when you're sad, on end when you're scared, curly when you're happy, etc.

Result 4: Ears that are...

1	...pointy, like an elf's
2	...small and rounded
3	...able to wiggle when you want them to
4	...big and floppy
5	...pointy, like a cat's
6	...adorned with one or more earrings

Result 5: A body that's unusually...

1	...flexible
2	...agile
3	...graceful
4	...small
5	...strong
6	...tall

Result	6: Clothes that are...
1	...always dirty and/or torn
2	...long and flowy
3	...polka-dotted wizard robes
4	...pajamas, slippers, and bathrobe
5	...the uniform of your school or a Coinworld sports team
6	...trendy and fashionable

Signature Features

Signature features are things that really stand out about your lil' Wizard — things that people would mention first when describing him. You don't need to have one of these, but it might be fun!

Like your basic appearance you can make up your own signature features, choose from the table, or leave it up to chance (this time by rolling two six-sided dice and adding them up to see what you get). You can roll more than once if you like, and if you don't like what the dice give you? Just roll again or choose something else!

Result	Signature Features
2	Antennae: like a butterfly? An alien? A radio or robot?
3	Scar: from falling out of the tree, or off your broom, or another event that makes a good story. What does your scar look like and where is it?
4	Tail: like a fox's tail? A lion's tail? Some other animal?
5	Glasses: are they round? Square? Half-moon? Sunglasses?
6	Birthmark: where is it? What is it shaped like? Does it sparkle or change color or have another unusual quality? Does it have a special meaning?
7	Squeaky shoes: what do they look like? What does the squeak sound like? Do they squeak all the time or just on certain surfaces?
8	Stylish cape: what color and fabric? Long, short, or in-between?
9	Rain boots: what color? Are they patterned?
10	Outrageous accent: it isn't from any known archipelagos
11	Bowtie that spins: what color? Solid or patterned? Bowties are cool!
12	Roll twice and use both results

Personality

Choose or roll your lil' Wizard's general nature, and then her best quality and her worst flaw. These parts of your Wizard's personality don't change your ratings either — you may be physically strong and still clumsy — but they'll help you tell your lil' Wizard's stories. When your clumsy Mage fails to lift something, perhaps she trips over her feet or loses her grip in the process.

Result	Best Quality
2	Optimistic: you always look on the bright side of life!
3	Generous: you're happy to share what you have with friends or strangers
4	Loyal: you would do anything for your friends, family, and/or school
5	Intelligent: you're smart and you value knowledge and thinking
6	Courageous: you don't let fear stand in your way
7	Friendly: you're easy to talk to and get along well with people
8	Imaginative: you can usually think of a creative solution
9	Altruistic: you put others — people and/or animals — ahead of yourself
10	Patient: you're not easily frustrated when things get difficult
11	Steadfast: you're not easily swayed once you've decided on something
12	Roll twice and use both results

Your lil' Wizard's Best Quality is probably one of the first things that comes to mind whenever someone speaks about her, but it should also be one of the first things you consider when deciding how to handle a problem. Always play to your strengths!

Result	General Nature
2	Grumpy: it typically takes a lot to make you happy
3	Shy: you're a bit nervous around new people
4	Cheerful: it typically takes a lot to make you sad
5	Cautious: you like to check things out before you act
6	Daring: you love excitement and rarely play it safe
7	Curious: you always want to know more about things
8	Silly: you don't take things very seriously and you often joke around
9	Finicky: it's very important to you that things are a particular way
10	Talkative: you have lots to say and you're always looking for an audience
11	Fidgety: you're a bit restless, and there's almost always something in your hands
12	Roll twice and use both results

Result	Worst Flaw
2	Lazy: you try not to do more than you really have to do
3	Fearful: your fear can get in the way of you doing things
4	Gossipy: you can't keep a secret and like to talk about other people
5	Foolhardy: you tend to take a lot of risky chances
6	Impulsive: you tend to act before you think
7	Clumsy: you often trip, fall, slip, and otherwise get in difficult situations
8	Stubborn: you seldom change your mind, even when given good reasons
9	Gullible: you tend to believe lies, exaggeration, and jokes
10	Tactless: you often speak before you think
11	Selfish: you commonly think about yourself first
12	Roll twice and use both results

If you're creating your first lil' Wizard, and especially if this is your first time roleplaying, you might want to pick a General Nature that's close to your own. That will make it easier to play. Later, you might find it fun to play someone completely different from you!

Your lil' Wizard's flaws are wonderful opportunities for amusing and dramatic moments in the game, but be careful not to let them ruin everyone's fun! Watch for chances to introduce them without interrupting or undermining the story, and you'll be fine.

Tastes

Define your lil' Wizard's preferences. What does he like? What does he *dislike*? What does he fear? What does he like to do for fun? These choices or rolls round out your Wizard as a whole person, and they can help you decide what to do in the Tales you tell together.

Remember: just like in real life, everyone likes, dislikes, fears, and dreams of different things, and it's a good idea to keep your friends' feelings in mind as you adventure together. Learning these things about your friends and their lil' Wizards is one of the greatest benefits of sharing a Tale.

Result	Your Lil' Wizard likes...
2	...shoes or hats or other accessories
3	...a particular food (like broccoli or green beans or Brussels sprouts, which we call Bone sprouts on Coinworld!)
4	...food and eating in general
5	...books
6	...music
7	...animals
8	...candy and/or other treats
9	...bugs
10	...math
11	...a place (like the beach or the forest or the mountains)
12	Roll twice and use both results

Result	Your Lil' Wizard enjoys...
2	...playing or watching sports
3	...camping
4	...flying on a broom
5	...reading
6	...singing and/or playing music
7	...playing games
8	...inventing
9	...cooking and/or baking
10	...fishing
11	...sleeping
12	Roll twice and use both results

Result	Your Lil' Wizard fears...
2	...heights and/or falling
3	...fire
4	...monsters
5	...flying
6	...the dark
7	...big animals
8	...being alone
9	...tight spaces
10	...spiders
11	...failure
12	Roll twice and use both results

Result	Your Lil' Wizard dislikes...
2	...lima beans or spinach or some other yucky food
3	...the color brown or maybe orange or bright green
4	...loud noises
5	...rain
6	...mint or black licorice or another strong flavor
7	...doing chores
8	...bugs
9	...the hot sun
10	...running and getting sweaty or dirty, especially in thick or heavy clothes
11	...tests, quizzes, and homework, though maybe only for one particular subject
12	Roll twice and use both results

Motivations

What does your lil' Wizard dream of doing someday? What does she want to be when she grows up? Why did she decide to go on an adventure? Knowing what your Wizard hopes to do and why she's adventuring can help you make decisions about what she does in your Tales. Maybe you'll even find a few chances to live out your lil' Wizard's dreams at the gaming table!

Result	Your Lil' Wizard dreams of...
2	...starting a Magic school of her very own and mentoring the next generation
3	...brewing a new kind of potion
4	...visiting every archipelago on Coinworld (on both sides!)
5	...finding something amazing and/or legendary
6	...becoming a famous Sorcerer or Mage, or just doing something really special
7	...discovering a new kind of plant or animal
8	...exploring a place no one's visited for centuries
9	...becoming Coinworld's fastest broom racer
10	...healing animals and/or people, maybe starting a magical hospital
11	...making her family proud
12	Roll twice and use both results

Result	Your Lil' Wizard seeks to...
2	...try out his new broom
3	...explore (finding new things is fun!)
4	...conquer his fear
5	...collect rare ingredients for a special potion
6	...fulfill a school requirement
7	...experience new cultures
8	...help people
9	...complete a rock collection
10	...find a long lost family member or friend
11	...spread understanding and acceptance of magic
12	Roll twice and use both results

Background

Summarize your lil' Wizard's childhood so far...

+ What archipelago did he grow up on? *See page 15 for a description of all the archipelagoes of Coinworld.* Does your lil' Wizard still live where he was raised, or has he moved? Is he used to living in a city or in a small town or in the country? Is his home near the coast, in a forest, on a hill, or somewhere else?

+ What's his family like? Any brothers or sisters? Did he grow up with his grandparents, aunts, uncles, and cousins living nearby?

+ If your Wizard is a lil' Mage, what school does he attend and what does he study? What are his teachers like?

+ If your Wizard is a lil' Sorcerer, who does he get his magical gifts from: his mom, dad, aunt, uncle, grandma, or grandpa? Or is it a mystery to everyone?

Traits

Your lil' Wizard has **Traits** that let you know what he can do in the Tale. The three Traits are **Body**, **Heart**, and **Brain**.

Body

Body covers your lil' Wizard's physical abilities: running, jumping, climbing, holding her breath, and so on. Any time your Wizard does something with her legs, feet, or muscles, that's Body!

Characters with a high Body tend to be athletic, physical, and healthy. They're strong, fast, and coordinated. They like to solve problems directly — they climb over a fence rather than finding a way around; they break down a door rather than picking the lock.

A high Body helps you...

+ Not catch the cold that's going around

+ Stay warm in a cold place

+ Run away from an angry alligator

+ Swing on a rope across a creek

+ Skip a stone across a lake

+ Stay absolutely still so you don't give away your hiding place

Heart

Heart is how your lil' Wizard interacts with other people and your inner self. Any time your Wizard wants to make a friend feel better, convince others to do what he says, or be brave even when he's scared, that's Heart!

Characters with a high Heart tend to be charming, caring, and friendly. They are also brave, inspiring, and persuasive. They make friends wherever they go. They like to solve problems by getting other people involved — they persuade someone to open a locked door for them, and they put themselves in other peoples' shoes.

A high Heart helps you...

+ Persuade the baker to give you a free cookie at the bakery

+ Not be persuaded to do something that might be a bad idea

+ Stay where you are when a wild animal roars at you

+ Convince a stranger to help you or offer you information

+ Make a good impression on the new headmaster

+ Talk your way out of trouble

Brain

Brain is about what your lil' Wizard knows and how quickly she figures things out. Any time your Wizard needs to work out a puzzle, fix a broken broom, or remember something that happened a long time ago, that's Brain!

Characters with a high Brain tend to be smart, clever, and well educated. They know a lot of things, they remember a lot of things, and they can figure out even more. They like to solve problems by thinking about them — they come up with unusual approaches, and use their knowledge and previous experience to figure out the best way to overcome troubles.

A high Brain helps you...

+ Accurately write a Magic formula during class

+ Invent a new potion

- Notice unusual details, like that purple ant crawling about

- Solve a goblin's riddle

- Remember a name, phrase, or other detail you heard long ago

- Figure out how the lock on the pantry door works, or identify how to start up a strange machine

Strengths and Weaknesses

Just like us, lil' Wizards are stronger in some ways and weaker in others. To reflect this, each of your Wizard's Traits is different...

- Pick one Trait in which your lil' Wizard is **Good**. When rolling dice with this Trait, your Wizard adds nothing (+0) to the roll.

- Pick a second Trait in which your lil' Wizard is **Better**. When rolling dice with this Trait, your Wizard adds +1 to the roll.

- The last Trait — the one you haven't chosen the other two times — is something in which your lil' Wizard is **Best**. When rolling dice with this Trait, your Wizard adds +2 to the roll.

You can pick these in any order, so long as you only pick each one once (so you have one Trait that's Good, one that's Better, and one that's Best).

Example: Megan is creating her character, a lil' Sorcerer named Mia. She decides that Mia is a brainiac, so she picks Brain to be Best (+2) for her. She then chooses Heart to be Better (+1) because Mia is nice but not very patient, and she likes to tease others. The only choice left is Good (+0), so that becomes Mia's Body. After all, she'd rather sit and read a book than play tag.

Powers

Your lil' Wizard's magical abilities are called Powers. Every lil' Wizard starts with the Broom Riding Power, plus two more.

Sorcerers choose two Powers from...

- **Alchemy:** brewing potions and the like

- **Divination:** identifying magic; looking into the past, present, or future

- **Spellcasting:** using charms to create various magical effects

Mages choose two Powers from...

- **Conjuring:** making objects and magical creatures appear out of nowhere

- **Shapechanging:** taking on the shape of an animal

- **Spellcasting:** using spells to create various magical effects

Mastery over these Powers is measured like Traits: when your lil' Wizard has a Power, she is either Good, Better, or Best with it and adds +0, +1, or +2 to dice rolls when using that Power.

Your Wizard doesn't start off quite as strong with his Powers as his Traits, though. Once your Wizard has three Powers, choose one with which your Wizard is Better (+1). He's automatically Good (+0) with his other two starting Powers.

Power Descriptions

So what can your lil' Wizard do with these Powers? All of the following, and anything else that makes sense to you and the Narrator!

ALCHEMY

Alchemy is the art of brewing magical potions, elixirs, and ointments. Components and a container are needed to perform Alchemy. Components are sometimes commonly available, sometimes rare, and sometimes funny. The most popular potions are healing ointments and potions that let you do amazing things like fly or have the strength of a giant, but alchemists invent all kinds of concoctions with strange effects!

BROOM RIDING

This important Power is a required for all lil' Wizards. It's used whenever your Wizard rides a flying broom — a difficult exercise, especially when weather isn't helping. The most skilled Wizards can perform spectacular aerial maneuvers like loop-de-loops and dive bombings.

CONJURING

Conjuring is the art of making objects and magical items appear out of nowhere. Conjuring requires the use of a magic wand. The easiest conjuring involves small items (candy, your broom, roller skates, pumpkin pie, flowers, etc.). It's possible to conjure magical items, if it fits the Tale and if the Narrator allows it. For example, a lil' Mage in an old mansion might conjure a magical key that opens nearly any door.

DIVINATION

Divination is the art of seeing into the past, the present, and the future of objects, locations, and people. Lil' Sorcerers can divine by looking into a mirror, tea leaves, or coffee grounds. They can examine an object to see its history: who it belonged to, how it was built, and when it was placed at a specific location. This Power works on magical effects and items too, so a Sorcerer with Divination can sense when magic was used in an area, or what an artifact might be able to do. Divination can also track a lost item, so long as you had it last.

SHAPECHANGING

Shapechanging is the art of turning into an animal for a limited time. To shift, a lil' Mage picks an animal that exists on Coinworld and that they've encountered before, like a cat or bird. Keep in mind that shifting into something tiny like an insect is incredibly dangerous, as the Mage could wind up being swatted by someone or something bigger!

SPELLCASTING

Spellcasting is the art of using spells (for Mages) or charms (for Sorcerers). Spellcasting requires the use of a magic wand. Spells and charms deliver magical effects (like making a stool dance or casting light in a dark area). They can also transmute objects (a math test into a comic book or stewed tomatoes into an apple pie), but the one thing they **can't** do is change people! For whatever reason, spells and charms simply have no effect on the minds and bodies of living beings.

Wizard Gear

A lil' Wizard is instantly recognized for four things she carries: the first is her mode of transportation: **a flying broom**; the second is her headgear: **a pointy hat**; the third is her tool for magic: her **wand**; and the fourth is a special animal: her **familiar**. All these things are special and often unique to her.

Your Broom

A must-have accessory for Sorcerers and Mages alike, the flying broom is a strange, marvelous, and often temperamental tool! Piloting such a "vehicle" is far from easy and it takes a lot of experience to reach perfect mastery. Also, every broom has its own nature, and adapting to a new broom requires even more practice, often at the risk of being dismounted over rough terrain, or even the ocean!

Describe your broom. What does it look like? What kind of personality does it have? It can't talk, but how does it behave? If you like, you can choose or roll for its personality just like you did for your Wizard (see page 26).

Your Hat

Pointy, colorful, and often oversized, a Wizard's hat is her emblem, and often her most precious belonging. Some hats are inherited while others are lovingly made by the wearer. A Wizard's hat is more than just head-gear — it's also a "business card" showing others the status and area of expertise of its owner. These details are conveyed by colored ribbons attached to the hat, some of which are awarded by characters the Wizard has helped, or headmasters proud of their graduates.

What does your hat look like? Was it handed down to you, and if so, from whom? If it was specially made, did you make it yourself or did someone else make it for you? What do the ribbons on your hat look like, and what do they say about you?

Your Wand

Wands are necessary for some kinds of magic, like Spellcasting and Conjuring, but even Wizards who don't focus on those kinds of magic have their own wands. Like hats, wands are often tailored to or by their owners, and they're always interesting: some are carved from rare wood, glow in unusual colors, or have precious gems embedded in them.

What kind of wood is your wand made of? What does it look like: is it straight and polished, or knotty and ancient? Does it have any other interesting features?

Your Familiar

Every lil' Wizard has an inseparable pet called a familiar, and these creatures not only help define who a Wizard is but also what she can do in her adventures *(see page 52 for more on the role of familiars in Tales)*. Long ago, familiars were all black cats, without exception, but today all kinds of animals are familiars, whether they're covered with fur, feathers, or scales. The one constant is that familiars are still always black, which can be pretty amusing when this isn't a common color for the species.

The most common familiars are cats, crows, and owls, but again, any animal on Coinworld is a possibility. Familiars can also come from the various animals that are unique to Coinworld, which are always identified with an adjective. Some examples are the snow monkeys and azure eagles of Steppes *(see page 83)* or the laughing bat of Shivers *(see page 101)*. You can make up your own unique animals as well if you want, and this is a great way to give your familiar a little flair.

Remember that your familiar will accompany you on all of your adventures. So while you could choose an elephant and it might be a lot of fun sometimes, he won't fit on your broom very easily — unless you can find a creative solution for getting him around. Likewise, a butterfly is beautiful but it might not be able to help you very often.

Describe and name your familiar. Remember that *all* familiars are black. Beyond your familiar's appearance, you might want to describe its personality.

Need some ideas? Here's a list for you to choose from, or you can let the dice decide (roll two dice and add them together, then pick anything on that line or another animal that's similar; or roll again if you don't like what you get).

Result	Your familiar is a...
2	...deer, gazelle, pony, or bison
3	...squirrel, chipmunk, mouse, or meerkat
4	...raccoon, possum, badger, or groundhog
5	...chameleon, gecko, iguana, or Gila monster
6	...dog, fox, wolf, or hyena
7	...hawk, kestrel, vulture, or condor
8	...blue jay, robin, sparrow, or chickadee
9	...monkey, chimpanzee, lemur, or red panda
10	...frog, toad, turtle, or salamander
11	...weasel, otter, beaver, or platypus
12	...duck, goose, swan, or chicken

Your Other Belongings

We all have a few treasured items that go everywhere with us. Maybe we cling to a stuffed animal, a photo album, or a small toy.

Lil' Wizards have their own treasures too, and your character is no exception. Choose three items that your character always has close at hand. Make sure they're small enough to carry! You may regret choosing that piano...

Drawing

It's the icing on the cake if you can draw your character. It's a great way to help the other players imagine what your character looks like. Don't forget her familiar as well!

Don't worry if you're not an artist, though. Some players are better at describing their lil' Wizards with words, and others are great at staying in character. Play to your strengths and you'll do fine.

Name

You're almost done! All you need to do is name your lil' Wizard and you're ready to have a few magical adventures in Coinworld.

Character Examples

Here are two detailed examples to help you understand character creation. Introducing... Mia and Toby!

Mia, Lil' Sorcerer

Mia is full of energy; she's impulsive and she sometimes likes to tease. This daredevil wants to show all of Coinworld what she can do.

She's tough but fair, and sometimes her curiosity gets her into trouble. She likes taking walks and watching the rain. She dislikes wind, especially when it takes her hat off, and she also has trouble with people who dismiss her because of her young age.

Like every Sorcerer, Mia has the Broom Riding Power. Her other Powers are Spellcasting and Divination.

HER TRAITS
Body: Good (+0)
Heart: Better (+1)
Brain: Best (+2)

HER POWERS
Broom Riding: Good (+0)
Spellcasting: Better (+1)
Divination: Good (+0)

HER BELONGINGS
A silver pendant she inherited from her great-grandmother
Her lucky coin
A tin whistle

HER WAND
Made from the wood of a wild walnut tree

HER FAMILIAR
Catatonic, an elegant and haughty black cat

Toby, Lil' Mage

Toby is a gentle and amazingly patient boy, although others tend to view him as hopelessly lazy. This sweet dreamer has an optimistic and protective nature, and he's also a goofball with a knack for getting into the most comical situations.

He likes to play hooky to go fishing or read comic books under a shady tree. He dislikes discipline and conflict.

Like every Mage, Toby has the Broom Riding Power. His other Powers are Conjuring and Shapechanging.

HIS TRAITS
Body: Better (+1)
Heart: Best (+2)
Brain: Good (+0)

HIS POWERS
Broom Riding: Better (+1)
Conjuring: Good (+0)
Shapechanging: Good (+0)

HIS BELONGINGS
A fishing pole with a magical fishing hook
A carved wood yoyo
His favorite rock

HIS WAND
Made of driftwood, decorated with a blue jay feather

HIS FAMILIAR
Helmer, a fat and wily crow who likes practical jokes

Basic Rules

Little Wizards is a game and just like any game there are rules, which are explained in this chapter. To help the Narrator, you'll also find a few reminders in the first Tale (*"Bewitched Chocolate!" on page 70*), as well as several "Note to the Narrator" sections throughout the book.

The rules are there to help everyone determine the outcome of a Tale's events. They come in whenever it's uncertain whether an Action succeeds, and whenever you need a little guidance as to what the outcome of an Action might be. For example...

- A lil' Sorcerer uses a charm to make a mean dog fall asleep. Does it work?

- A lil' Mage wants to change into a bird to follow a flight of wild geese. Can she do it?

- A cook prepares a coconut cake. Will it be tasty?

- A schoolboy works on a difficult math problem. Does he solve it?

As you can see, the rules can come in whether magic is being used or not.

Remember that the rules are there to *help* determine what happens, *not* to dictate what happens. It's still important that everyone add to the story, and in a lot of cases that's actually all you'll need — the rules won't be necessary because success or failure, and their outcomes, are obvious. You don't need the rules when you're reading in a known language, for example.

Whenever there's a question about what actually happens in your Tale, whether the rules are used or not, the Narrator has the last word. It's the Narrator's job to make sure the game runs smoothly, and her biggest job is to act as referee when the rules are used.

Actions

An **Action** occurs any time a character tries to do something that may not succeed, or may not turn out as expected (like showing off by jumping rope, baking a complicated cake recipe, or walking along a thin tree trunk to cross a river).

Using a Power can also be an Action, if there's a chance of failure or unexpected results. The rules for using Powers are slightly different than regular Actions, and are explained on page 46.

Taking an Action involves a **Trait**, a **Difficulty**, and a **die roll**. We'll talk more about each of these in the following sections.

The Trait

Every Action is linked to one of the character's Traits (Heart, Body, or Brain). The Narrator decides which Trait is used to attempt each Action.

Example: Mia wants to swim across a large, deep pond. The Narrator decides that this is a Body Action because it's mostly physical. Meanwhile, Toby wants to mend his sister's broken doll, and the Narrator asks him to use the Brain Trait because it's mostly about figuring out how the pieces go back together.

The Difficulty

Every Action has a Difficulty, which is also decided by the Narrator. An Action's Difficulty is determined by the situation — the harder the Action, the higher the Difficulty. There are six Difficulties to choose from,

> ## Note to the Narrator: What Trait to Roll
>
> *There are lots of Actions the players might try that could involve two or even all three of the Traits. Is trying to spot something in the dark a Body roll (eyesight) or a Brain roll (picking out what's important)? A good argument could be made for either, and in cases like this it's the Narrator's job to decide which makes the most sense. When in doubt, it's entirely fine to let the player roll with the highest of the Traits that might apply.*

each with a minimum Result needed for the Action to succeed. (We'll explain Results in a lil' bit.)

Here are the six Difficulties...

Difficulty	Minimum Result
Very Easy	5
Easy	6
Average	7
Hard	8
Very Hard	9
Almost Impossible	10

Determining the Difficulty

How do you decide how difficult an Action is? Unless magic is being used, this is easy — just ask yourself, "How difficult would this be in real life?" If you think it would be hard, then make the Difficulty Hard (8). If you think it would be very easy to do, then make the Difficulty Very Easy (5).

Example: Mia is climbing a ladder, which the Narrator knows is pretty simple in real life, so he decides it's a Very Easy (5) Action. If the ladder is rickety and there's a lot of wind, or maybe if she's also holding a heavy and awkward bag in her hands, the Narrator might decide it's Hard (8). If in addition to all that Mia is also blindfolded and it's raining cats and dogs, well, the Narrator's probably going to decide it's Almost Impossible (10)!

Magic is a little more complicated since there are no real world examples. When magic is being used, it's easiest to ask how complex the Action would be without magic (assuming it's possible). For instance, casting a spell to clear the dinner table is probably Easy (6), since clearing the table is pretty easy without magic. Likewise, using a charm to dig a hole in tightly packed dirt is probably Hard (8), just like it would be without the charm.

Of course, magic can do lots of things that are impossible without it, like lifting the dinner table into the air or digging a hole through concrete. These Actions require a better idea of what magic can and can't do to help determine how hard they are, and for that we've got a whole section on magic in the game (*see Using Powers, page 46*).

The Die Roll

When you attempt an Action, a die roll determines whether it succeeds or fails. Roll two six-sided dice (2d6) and add the results together. Then add the bonus you get from the Trait or Power being used: +0 for Good, +1 for Better, or +2 for Best. The total you get is called your **Result**.

Example: Mia rolls 2d6. The first die shows 4 and the second die shows 5. Her roll is a 9 (4 + 5). She's attempting a Heart Action and her Heart is Better (+1), so she adds 1 to the roll. Her final Result is 10.

You may sometimes also get bonuses from other things, like Teamwork (*see page 43*).

Resolving an Action

Remember, an Action's Difficulty determines the minimum Result required to succeed. This is shown on the Difficulty Table, which you can find on page 40.

Difficulties run from 5 (Very Easy) to 10 (Almost Impossible), and if your total Result — your total die roll + whatever bonus you get from the Trait or Power being used — ties or beats the Difficulty, you succeed!

First Example: Mia climbs a tree to rescue a frightened kitten. The Narrator decides this is a Body Action with a Difficulty of Average (7). Since Mia's Body is Good (+0), she makes the roll without a bonus. The total of her die roll must be 7 or higher for her to succeed.

Second Example: Toby asks for a free cookie at his favorite bakery. The Narrator decides the baker is stingy and not very nice, so the Difficulty is Hard (8), and also decides that this is a Heart Action. Toby's Heart is Best (+2), so to get the minimum Result of 8 needed to succeed, he'll need to roll a 6 or more on the dice.

Third Example: Estelle is playing chess against Mr. Popov, the chess champion of Steppes, and the Narrator rightly decides this is a Brain Action. Estelle's Brain is Best (+2), but the Narrator also decides that the Difficulty is Almost Impossible (10). After all, Mr. Popov is the chess champion of an entire archipelago! Estelle has her work cut out for her — she will need a die roll total of 8 or higher to win the game, since 8 plus her Brain bonus of +2 is the minimum Result of 10.

Disaster!

When both dice come up 1, the Action fails and the acting character faces a **Disaster!** Everything goes wrong for the character and his Action fails in some catastrophic way. Disasters should always be dramatic, and often amusing! However, they should never leave the players unable to move forward in the Tale.

First Example: Climbing the tree to rescue the kitten, Mia rolls double 1s. It's a Disaster! She slips out of the tree, breaking a few branches and maybe her wand on the way down. The kitten finds this funny enough that he isn't frightened any more. He climbs down on his own and rubs up against Mia to make her feel better.

Second Example: Trying to convince the baker to give him a cookie, Toby rolls double 1s. Disaster! Not only does Toby not get a cookie but the baker blusters and her face turns bright red. Toby dodges out of the shop and should probably go to the bakery down the street for the next week or two, but he doesn't get in any trouble for asking.

Third Example: In her chess game against the Steppish champion, Estelle rolls double 1s. Disaster! She momentarily forgets an important rule of chess, moving her rook diagonally or her king three spaces. She certainly won't win this match, but she may end up inventing a whole new game!

Brilliant Success!

When both dice come up 6, the Action is a **Brilliant Success!** The character gets everything she was hoping for and more.

First Example: While rescuing the kitten from the tree, Mia rolls double 6s — a Brilliant Success! In no time she reaches the top branches, and her speed and dexterity are so amazing that the squirrels living in the tree are jealous. As Mia slides back down the tree with the kitten safe in her arms, the squirrels scurry off to tell their animal friends. Perhaps Mia will run into the squirrels and their friends again, and if she does her Brilliant Success will be remembered fondly.

Second Example: Bartering with the baker for a cookie, Toby rolls double 6s. Brilliant Success! The baker is impressed with Toby's argument and happily gives him two cookies, plus a half dozen more to share with his friends.

Third Example: In her match against the chess champion, Estelle rolls double 6s. Brilliant Success! She finds a way to use a new opening she's been working on, and she executes it perfectly. Everyone's amazed and impressed by the skill of this young player, even her opponent Mr. Popov!

Teamwork

Friends help each other out. When two or more characters work together on an Action, the character making the roll gets a +1 bonus for each friend who helps. It's up to the Narrator to decide how many friends can reasonably lend a hand and still be helpful; usually, once you have more than two helpers, people start getting in each other's way.

Only one character rolls for the Action. When one character is clearly taking the Action and getting help from the other(s), the character taking the Action makes the roll. If the characters are working as a team, the character who's best with the Trait or Power being used makes the roll. If there's a tie, the Narrator decides who makes the roll.

Example: Mia is trying to lift a heavy box. The Difficulty is Average (7). If Mia does it alone, she needs to roll a 7 because her Body is Good (+0).

Estelle could offer some advice ("Lift with your knees!"), giving Mia a +1 bonus. In this case Mia's still making the roll and needs to get a 6 thanks to Estelle's bonus.

Maybe Toby is also around and can help lift the box.

Now there are two characters lifting with Estelle directing, so who makes the roll? Toby has the higher Body — Better (+1) — so the Narrator decides he makes the roll with a +2 bonus from Estelle's advice and Mia helping to lift. Toby only needs to roll a 4 to succeed against the Difficulty of Average (7) thanks to his Body bonus and the Teamwork bonuses from his friends.

Make Failures Interesting

What does it mean when an Action fails? It mostly depends on the situation, the players, and the Tale you're telling. Failure can mean a lot of different things based on how you want the Tale to proceed, but two things are always true: failures should always be interesting, and they should never bring the Tale to a halt. Here are a few ways you can accomplish this...

Not that Way!

If the Action isn't critical to moving the Tale forward, a failure may simply mean that the Action isn't possible, at least not by that character in that situation. If the character wants to succeed with the Action, she'll have to find another way to do it.

Example: Mia is trying to climb a tree but fails her Body roll. This could mean that she can't find a strong low branch, so climbing isn't an option — unless she can change the situation (say, for example, by finding a ladder).

Obstacle!

Failure can introduce some kind of obstacle that lets the character roll again but with the Difficulty one higher than before. If the second roll also fails, the character probably needs a new approach (as described under "Not that Way!").

Example: The tree Mia is trying to climb has lots of close, thick branches, so the Narrator decides making the ascent is Easy (6). The dice are not kind and Mia still fails the roll, so the Narrator declares that, while the lowest branch is weaker than Mia expected and breaks, she can still jump up to reach a higher one. With this obstacle in mind, the second Action's Difficulty is is now Average (7), one step higher than Easy.

Complications!

If the Action is critical to moving the Tale forward, you may want to turn a failure into a success... with complications. In this case the Action succeeds so the Tale can keep going, but something happens that makes the character's life more difficult moving forward.

Example: The kitten that Mia is trying to rescue from the tree has an important clue on his collar, and that clue is the only way Mia will figure out where to go next in the Tale. Mia has to climb the tree, so the Narrator treats a failure as a success instead — but introduces a complication. In the process of climbing the tree, Mia annoys a squirrel, which follows her around for a while after, pelting her with acorns and chattering in outrage. This makes it harder for Mia to do other things later in the Tale.

Setback!

Failure can result in a lingering setback like an injury or used up spell component. A setback increases the Difficulty of Actions with a particular Trait or Power for a limited time. The Difficulty increase should only be one higher, and the setback should only last as long as makes sense in the story.

Example: Mia fails her Body roll and falls out of the tree. The Narrator decides she twists her ankle, so all of her Body rolls are one Difficulty higher until the swelling goes down.

Tough Decision!

To give the player a little more say in the outcome, a failure could become a tough decision for the character to make. Tough decisions should always be just that... tough. There shouldn't be any obviously better choices — the character has to choose between two or more undesirable outcomes.

Example: As Mia tumbles out of the tree, the Narrator offers her the chance to grab hold of another branch to break her fall — but there's a brownie perched on the branch that she'll knock off if she grabs hold.

On the one hand, brownies are annoying practical jokers. Mia's player might decide that saving herself is worth possibly injuring the mischievous creature, but there's also the chance that this brownie or another one might try to get back at her with pranks for a while.

On the other hand, the player might decide that Mia is too kind to harm any creature, in which case she'll wind up twisting her ankle as described in the "Setback!" section. The Narrator might immediately reward her by having the brownie use magic to cushion her fall, or maybe the brownie follows her around to help her later. Or maybe the brownie is simply scared off by the falling girl and she has to wait for the swelling to subside.

Not knowing how the situation will play out is what makes this a tough decision.

Another Player Narrates!

Lastly, failure is an opportunity to let *another player* decide what happens. You never know... She might come up with something you never thought of! Some players may find failure more fun if they have some say in what it means for their friends.

Just remember that the Action is still a failure — letting another player decide what happens isn't their chance to turn the roll into a success. It's also not their chance to turn the roll into a Disaster! Be creative, but also be fair.

Example: When Mia fails her Body roll to climb the tree, the Narrator can't come up with a way to make the failure interesting, so he lets Estelle's player decide what happens. She thinks for a moment and describes Mia landing far out on the edge of a branch high off the ground. The branch creaks ominously and there's no easy way to get back to the tree trunk or down to the other Wizards. What will Mia do?

Using Powers

When a character uses a Power to perform an Action, the rules are only slightly different. First the player tells the Narrator what she's trying to do with her Power...

First Example: Estelle intends to brew a Potion of Giant Strength.

Second Example: Toby wants to shapechange into a rabbit.

Third Example: Mia needs to ride her broom to meet up with her friends. Normally this wouldn't require a roll, but she's in a particular hurry.

Of course, the character needs to *have* the Power she wants to use...

First Example: Estelle needs Alchemy to prepare her potion.

Second Example: Toby needs Shapechanging to turn into a rabbit.

Third Example: Like all Wizards, Mia has the Broom Riding Power, so she's good to go.

Next, the Narrator assigns a Difficulty just like any other Action *(see page 40)*: it can be Very Easy (5), Easy (6), Average (7), Hard (8), Very Hard (9), or Almost Impossible (10).

First Example: A Potion of Giant Strength is pretty complex, so the Narrator sets the Difficulty for brewing it at Hard (8).

Second Example: Rabbits are fairly common, so taking the shape of one is Easy (6).

Third Example: It's a pretty breezy day but not enough to get in the way of broom riding, so Mia's Difficulty to ride to her friends in time is Average (7). If she were trying to get to them in a heavy rainstorm, perhaps it would be Hard (8), or even worse!

Finally, the player rolls two six-sided dice and adds them together, then adds the bonus from the Power she's using to get the Result. If this ties or beats the minimum Result needed for the Difficulty *(see page 40)*, the character successfully uses her Power!

Magical Disaster!

Even with Magic or Sorcery, bad things happen. When double 1s are rolled, the Action is a Disaster! and the outcome isn't at all what the character expected. The Narrator decides what happens, usually introducing a funny or ridiculous side-effect of the Power. This side-effect shouldn't be particularly dangerous or harmful, but there's no reason it can't seem that way at first.

First Example: While brewing her potion, Estelle rolls double 1s. It's a Disaster! The Narrator decides that whoever drinks the potion gains the strength of a mouse rather than a giant. Hm... Not what Estelle wanted but she still might be able to use the elixir...

Second Example: Toby rolls double 1s and... nothing happens, or so it seems. In the next room, his school's headmaster now sports rabbit ears. Talk about a Disaster!

Third Example: Mia wills her broom forward and rolls... double 1s! Oh no, it's a Disaster! Her broom lurches backward instead of forward and she can't make it stop!

Brilliant Success!

Fortunately, it's also possible to score a Brilliant Success with Sorcery and Magic. Double 6s mean the Power is especially helpful or its effects go beyond anything the lil' Wizard hoped.

First Example: Estelle gets double 6s on her Alchemy roll. Brilliant Success! Her Potion of Giant Strength not only works just like she wanted, it lasts longer than usual and tastes delicious!

Second Example: Toby's Shapechanging roll turns up double 6s — a Brilliant Success! He easily slips into his new form and his guise is so convincing it would even fool a *real* rabbit.

Third Example: Mia is all smiles as she rolls double 6s. Not only will her Brilliant Success get her to her friends in time, she'll have enough to spare that she can show off with some graceful loop-de-loops along the way.

Teamwork and Powers

When two characters have the same Power, they can use them together. Each lil' Wizard who helps another like this gives a +1 bonus to the character making the roll.

The Narrator decides the maximum number of characters who can help; and even when there doesn't appear to be a sensible limit, it's best to have no more than a couple helpers. Magic can go haywire when too many characters are involved.

Only one character rolls for the Action. When one character is clearly using her Power and getting help from the other(s), the character using her Power makes the roll. If the characters are working as a team, the character who's best with the Power being used makes the roll. If there's a tie, the Narrator decides who makes the roll.

Example: Toby is trying to catch a bird while flying on his broom. The Narrator decides the Difficulty is Hard (8). Alone, he needs to roll a 7 because his Broom Riding rating is Better (+1).

If Estelle uses Divination to determine where the bird will fly next and projects this into the sky for Toby to see, she gives him a +1 bonus with his roll.

Now let's say that Mia is also riding her broom nearby and she swoops in to help push the bird in Toby's direction. This adds another +1, and since they're both directly taking the Action there's a question of who rolls. Mia's Broom Riding is only Good (+0), so Toby still rolls because he's Better (+1). Toby needs to roll a 6 on the dice to catch the bird.

Sometimes another character simply won't be able to help with an Action using a Power, especially if they don't have the same Power themselves. The Narrator decides when this happens, and in these cases the best the other character can do is root for a high roll.

Example: To catch the bird Toby instead uses Conjuring to make a floating cage appear in its path. The Narrator decides this Action is mainly about willing the cage into existence rather than placing the cage or directing the bird into it, so neither Estelle nor Mia can help.

Difficulty and Powers

Powers used by lil' Sorcerers and Mages are only limited by their imaginations, and therefore yours. As a result, it can sometimes be tricky to determine just how Difficult an Action using a Power should be. Fortunately, there are plenty of common examples to draw from, including the following.

ALCHEMY

The Difficulty of Alchemy depends on how much magic is needed to achieve the desired effect. For instance, lots of plants and herbs can naturally help bring down a fever, so brewing a similar potion would be pretty easy. Nothing in nature lets you converse with animals, however, so that would be much harder.

+ **Very Easy (5):** brew a potion that brings down a fever, gets rid of a headache, or warms you up

+ **Easy (6):** create a compress that stops bleeding, a mixture that removes stains from fabric, or a potion that helps you stay awake

+ **Average (7):** brew a Potion of Bravery, a mixture to remove ink spills from paper, or a spice that makes everything you eat taste like your favorite food (particularly useful when trying new, unusual foods and not wanting to insult your hosts)

+ **Hard (8):** brew a Potion of Giant's Strength, a Potion of Owl's Senses to help you hear things that are very quiet, or a Potion of Gazelle's Grace to help you leap lightly over things

- **Very Hard (9):** brew a Potion of Invisibility, an oil you can pour into broken machinery to fix it, or a piece of chewing gum that lets you understand and converse with all kinds of animals

- **Almost Impossible (10):** brew a Salve of Protection against Fire, a potion that lets you breathe underwater, or a lotion that lets you be in two places at once

BROOM RIDING

The Difficulty of Broom Riding is based on the maneuver being attempted, the weather, and any terrain that's nearby (like mountains or castle towers), plus any other conditions that might get in the way.

- **Very Easy (5):** land in just the right spot in an open clearing, stay level through a light wind, or make a wide turn in a broom race

- **Easy (6):** streak over cars in a big tunnel, slowly float through a crowd in a dense fog, or navigate a sparse forest

- **Average (7):** fly faster than usual, make a tight circle through a strong wind, or evade a giant's swinging club

- **Hard (8):** speed over the heads of shoppers in a busy store, find your way through a heavy dust storm, or steer with the sun in your eyes

- **Very Hard (9):** perform a flawless loop-de-loop, dodge lightning in a dense electrical storm, or draft behind a soaring giant eagle

- **Almost Impossible (10):** slip under a moving wagon, fly through a tornado, or weave around an angry dragon

CONJURING

The Difficulty of Conjuring depends on how familiar you are with the item or creature being created, as well as how complex, large, and/or magical it is.

- **Very Easy (5):** conjure a cookie, hammer, or cup of water

- **Easy (6):** conjure a berry pie, pair of scissors, book, or a whole new outfit

- **Average (7):** conjure a meal, toolkit, or bathtub full of water

- **Hard (8):** conjure a banquet, bicycle, or bed

- **Very Hard (9):** conjure a magical seashell that lets you understand any language spoken to you, a wooden shelter to sleep in, or a typewriter

- **Almost Impossible (10):** conjure a car, a magical key that can open any door, or a refrigerator

DIVINATION

The Difficulty of Divination is based on how hard it would be to learn the desired information through other means.

- **Very Easy (5):** learn the name of an item's owner, learn the name of the last person to hold an item, or determine if any magic has recently been used in the area

- **Easy (6):** learn an item's origin, locate nearby secret doors and hidden passages, or sense another person's emotions

- **Average (7):** identify when a character is lying, know that a friend is in danger, or see through an illusion

- **Hard (8):** learn what recently happened at your location, send and receive short messages with a far away friend, or pinpoint the location of an item's owner

- **Very Hard (9):** locate a particular item, determine how to use a magical item, or consult your crystal ball for a Narrator hint about the Tale

- **Almost Impossible (10):** see what's happening at a location far away, hear a conversation over a great distance, or glean the history of a rare magical item

SHAPECHANGING

The Difficulty of Shapechanging depends on the size of the animal you want to turn into, as well as how familiar you are with it.

- **Very Easy (5):** transform into a dog, cat, or whatever your familiar is

- **Easy (6):** transform into a crow, goat, or badger

- **Average (7):** transform into an eagle, snow monkey, or horse

- **Hard (8):** transform into a dolphin, bear, or tiger

- **Very Hard (9):** transform into a mouse, elephant, or yak

- **Almost Impossible (10):** transform into a mosquito, whale, or dragon

SPELLCASTING

The Difficulty of Spellcasting is based on how unusual the desired effect is — how out of place it seems in the environment where it appears, or to those who see it after it's created. For example, summoning a gentle wind is simple and won't seem out of place at all. Walking through a wall, however, will probably raise some eyebrows if it's noticed, and it's pretty spectacular even if no one's around.

+ **Very Easy (5):** summon a gentle wind, restack a toppled pile of books, or turn on a light from across the room

+ **Easy (6):** become as light as a feather while falling, understand and speak an unfamiliar language, or know directions as though you have a compass

+ **Average (7):** grant an animal the ability to talk, track a person or animal, or create a new source of light

+ **Hard (8):** call a small thunderstorm, make an object bigger or smaller, or grow a flower from a seed in just a few minutes

+ **Very Hard (9):** animate a doll and project your voice through it, teleport a spider web from your doorway to a nearby shrub, or make you and your friends invisible

+ **Almost Impossible (10):** walk through a wall, make a forest sing and dance, or halt a raging flood or avalanche

Playing Familiars

Every lil' Wizard has a companion animal, a loyal friend who can offer help and sometimes advice. This animal is called a familiar, and it travels everywhere the Wizard goes, never leaving his side.

In the game, each player takes the role of both his Wizard and a familiar. However, he doesn't play *his* character's familiar — he plays the familiar of *another* player character! The rule is very simple...

Each player's familiar is played by the person sitting to the right.

Example: Tim, Megan, and Emily are playing *Little Wizards* in their living room. Megan is sitting to Tim's right, so she plays the role of Tim's familiar; Emily is sitting to Megan's right, so she plays Megan's familiar; and since Tim is sitting to Emily's right he plays the role of her familiar. Easy, right?

Familiars in Your Tale

Familiars are animals, even if they are a bit magical. The way they help and interact with other characters should stick to their basic nature. Dogs are loyal but easily distracted by interesting sights and sounds. Cats are stealthy but often nap if they're bored. Birds can fly but aren't much help lifting anything heavy. Ferrets are excellent spies but they also love pranks, which can be a problem for a lil' Wizard who dislikes surprises.

Each player described her familiar when she created her character (*see page 35*). Her choices should also be kept in mind when playing the familiar. For example, if she described her kitten familiar as ferocious and prone to hissing at much larger creatures, it wouldn't be right to play the kitten as meek and shy.

Don't forget that familiars can often help with Teamwork Actions, as described in the sidebar on page 44. Familiars are there to help and advice their Wizards, and they're generally happy to pitch in whenever and however they can.

That said, familiars are also characters, just like the lil' Wizards. They have their own personalities, opinions, and interests, and they sometimes disagree with their owners, especially when a Wizard is obviously doing something dangerous or foolish. This isn't a reason to play a familiar as mean or disruptive — it just means that sometimes their advise might not support what the lil' Wizards are doing.

Familiars also make mistakes and sometimes get into trouble, just like anyone else. Part of a Tale might involve rescuing someone's familiar, or visiting a familiar's home and helping solve one of its problems.

Roleplaying familiars is a great way to get into your Tale and really bring the story to life. It's also a great way to gain Lil' Points, which you can use to improve your Wizard (we talk more about these later, but you can skip forward if you like — Lil' Points are described on page 57).

Note to the Narrator: Playing Familiars

Familiars are described on the character sheet for the lil' Wizard they belong to. You may want to have the players copy their familiar's description on a note card and pass it to the player on their right to help that player roleplay the animal.

Example of Play

To demonstrate what a *Little Wizards* game looks like, let's observe this group of players: Paul, Megan, Tim, and Emily. Paul is the **Narrator** and has explained the rules and described Coinworld to the others. Megan, Tim, and Emily created their characters with his help.

Megan plays **Mia**, an ambitious and determined lil' Sorcerer who wants to show Coinworld what she can do. She knows Spellcasting and Divination.

Tim plays **Toby**, an easily distracted but well-meaning lil' Mage who is always ready to help and get his friends out of trouble. He can conjure items and shapechange into animals.

Emily plays **Estelle**, a quiet, thoughtful, and studious lil' Sorcerer who is interested in the history of Magic and Sorcery. She can prepare magic potions and elixirs, and she knows Spellcasting.

Mia, Toby, and Estelle are longtime friends, just like the kids who are playing them.

Paul, the Narrator, has prepared the Tale they're going to tell together. It starts like this...

Narrator: It's a beautiful morning — sunny, breezy, not too hot. Just the way you like it. Especially you, Toby.

It's the perfect day for a walk, to relax and have fun. You've decided to have a picnic along the Froth, the river near your home.

Tim: I'm wearing my new hat — the one with an adjustable visor to protect me from the sun. I also have my state-of-the-art yoyo, with an elastic string!

Narrator: Sounds good. How about you girls — did you bring anything special?

Emily: I have a wicker picnic basket, filled with sandwiches, a bottle of fruit juice, a few apples, and napkins.

Ah! I also have my Alchemy Spellbook, so I can review the latest formulas I've learned...

Megan: I have nothing special. I just want to rest today.

Tim: Yup! Today's a vacation. Come on, Estelle, you're not seriously going to stay buried in books. Not today!

Narrator: You walk and chat, and soon hear the river.

Emily: Yeah, we're almost there!

Narrator: As the trail turns to the right around a great oak tree, you reach the river. It's beautiful and cool.

Emily: Cool! I take the checkered tablecloth out of the basket and lay it on the grass close to the shore.

Tim: I'm going to see if there are fish!

Megan: I look around, just in case...

Narrator: Estelle sets up the picnic. Toby's bugging the poor fish that were minding their own business, and Mia keeps an eye out. The forest's edge is about ten yards from the shore, and you see mountaintops in the distance. You hear crickets and feel the warm sun... It's a little piece of heaven!

Emily: Lunch is ready!

Tim (licking his lips): Perfect. I'm starving!

Narrator: You sit around the tablecloth and you're about to take a bite of your sandwiches when suddenly there's movement in a nearby shrub! A gray squirrel darts out of the bushes, chased by a wild cat. If you don't do something, the poor little creature is going to get eaten right in front of you!

Megan: I cast a charm to keep the squirrel safe!

Narrator: Okay. You use your Spellcasting Power. Since you're a little surprised, the Action is Hard, so you need a Result of 8. Go ahead and roll two six-sided dice!

Megan (rolls the dice): 3... and 6! That adds up to 9, plus 1 for my bonus is 10! I made it!

Narrator: Good job! Roots erupt from the ground and straighten in front of the cat, who hits them running. He's stunned for a moment, then turns around and flees into the woods, his tail between his legs!

Megan: That'll teach him!

Narrator: The squirrel is out of breath and sits on his hind legs a couple yards away from you. He holds one of his legs up like it's hurt.

Emily: Poor little critter! I want to prepare a healing potion for him.

Narrator: Sure. You need a few herbs, but luckily they grow along the river. Since you're Better at Alchemy and the Difficulty is Easy, you need to roll a 5 or higher.

Emily (rolls the dice): 8, it succeeds by plenty!

Narrator: The potion takes a few minutes to prepare. The squirrel is still a bit scared, but also curious about what you're doing. Finally, the potion is ready.

Emily: I pour some into the lid of the fruit juice bottle and push it toward him.

Narrator: The squirrel is hesitant and sniffs the potion before drinking it. He seems to like the taste! His leg heals quickly, and he runs around happily before leaping onto your shoulder, chirping in thanks.

And the game goes on this way, until the end of the Tale...

Experience and Skills

Once you're familiar and comfortable with the Basic Rules (and ideally after you've played "Bewitched Chocolate!" on page 70), you might want to add the rules in this chapter. They let you improve your lil' Wizard's Traits and Powers over time, and introduce something new for her to learn: Skills.

Experience

Your lil' Wizard can experience many adventures on Coinworld, and through these adventures she will learn new things — she will visit new locations, meet new people, and encounter new animals and plants. She may even discover a few new tricks about magic. She will overcome challenges and solve problems, and over time her confidence, knowledge, and ability will grow. In the process she will earn **experience**, which she can spend to improve her Traits and Powers, and even learn new ones!

To measure the experience earned by the Wizards, the Narrator gives out Lil' Points, or LP for short. Lil' Points are earned at the end of each Tale, and the amount earned depends on many things: the Wizards' choices; what they discovered; the ideas they had (especially the good ones, but why not reward the not-so-good choices too if everyone had fun with them?); and also how well the players portrayed their characters and each others' familiars.

Between games, each Wizard can spend Lil' Points to get better at doing various things, as described in the "Spending Lil' Points" section (*see page 59*). First though, let's talk about how Lil' Points are earned...

Awarding Lil' Points

Most of the time, awarding 15 to 20 Lil' Points per Tale is fair. It offers the players some options immediately, and more if they want to save some points for later.

Lil' Points are earned for lots of things, but the general rule of thumb is that whenever one or more lil' Wizards do something inventive, clever, funny, or helpful, they earn Lil' Points. Sometimes they'll earn more than 1 LP at a time. Here's a list of nine common reasons lil' Wizards earn LP...

+ For completing a Tale: 5 LP

+ For roleplaying your lil' Wizard well: 2 LP

+ For roleplaying another Wizard's familiar well: 2 LP

+ For working with others to do something positive: 2 LP

+ For making the others laugh: 1 LP

- For using Magic or Sorcery in an interesting way: 1 LP

- For helping or consoling one of the Tale's characters: 1 LP

- For discovering a Coinworld location, character, or creature: 1 LP

- For heroism, a brilliant idea, or another action that makes the story more fun: 1 LP

Most of these can happen multiple times in a Tale. For instance, a player who does a great job roleplaying a familiar might earn 6 or 8 LP during the course of the game just for that.

The Narrator awards all Lil' Points, usually as soon as there's a reason to award them. For example, the Narrator might give each lil' Wizard 2 Lil' Points right after a great conversation in which everyone spoke and acted like their characters. He might also award an additional LP to one of the players for making everyone else laugh, and an additional 2 LP to those who also did an outstanding job playing familiars.

Don't worry if you miss an opportunity to award Lil' Points. They can be handed out when you remember, or all together at the end of a Tale. Some Narrators may prefer to hold off awarding Lil' Points entirely until the end of a Tale, either because it's easier to keep track of everything then or to avoid having the rewards get in the way of the story.

Anyone can recommend that another character deserves a Lil' Point or two, but it's selfish to recommend yourself. Selfishness isn't what lil' Wizards stand for, and it shouldn't be rewarded, even when you're really proud of yourself. Let the others recommend you when you do something special, and remember to do the same for them.

Example: When falling out of a tree, Mia has the chance to grab hold of a branch where a brownie is sitting. She can break her fall but might injure the creature in the process. She decides to risk injuring herself and doesn't grab the branch, a heroic decision that deserves to be rewarded. It wouldn't be fitting for Megan to recommend her Wizard earn a Lil' Point for the deed, but it would be just fine for Tim or Emily to do so.

The Narrator is still the final judge on when Lil' Points are earned, though! If you've already given each of the players 12 to 15 LP and there's still a lot more to the game or Tale, it might be a good idea to slow things down for a bit.

You might want to keep a bowl of small objects nearby while you play — maybe glass beads, pennies, or marbles — so you can give them out as Lil' Points are earned and everyone can easily see how many they have. Be careful if you use edible tokens like candy, because they might get eaten before they can be counted up!

Spending Lil' Points

Lil' Points are spent at the end of a Tale, or between two Tales. This is the time when lil' Wizards have an opportunity to learn from what they've seen and done, and it's also a good time to practice with new things.

It isn't necessary to spend all your Lil' Points right away; you can carry over some or all of them from one Tale to another, saving up for something big (some improvements cost more than others). Here are the things you can do when you spend Lil' Points...

IMPROVE A TRAIT

You can spend Lil' Points to improve one of your lil' Wizard's Traits (Body, Heart, or Brain).

+ Improve a Trait from Good to Better: 15 LP

+ Improve a Trait from Better to Best: 25 LP

Example: Emily has saved 15 Lil' Points after a few Tales. She decides to spend them on Estelle's Body Trait, improving it from Good (+0) to Better (+1). She'll need a lot more experience — and 25 more LP — before she can improve it again to Best (+2)!

IMPROVE A POWER

You can spend Lil' Points to improve one of the Powers your lil' Wizard already has.

+ Improve a Power from Good to Better: 15 LP

+ Improve a Power from Better to Best: 25 LP

Example: Mia's Broom Riding is Good (+0), which is fine but she wants to win more races with her friends. To improve from Good (+0) to Better (+1) she needs to spend 15 Lil' Points, and to improve from Better (+1) to Best (+2) she needs to spend 25 Lil' Points after that.

LEARN THE FOURTH POWER

At the start of your game, each lil' Wizard has the Broom Riding Power and picks two other Powers from three possibilities: Spellcasting, Alchemy, and Divination for Sorcerers; and Spellcasting, Shapechanging, and Conjuring for Mages. That leaves one Power each starting Wizard doesn't have yet.

You can spend Lil' Points to learn this last Power. When your lil' Wizard learns her fourth Power, it always starts at Good (+0).

+ Learn the fourth Power: 20 LP

Example: Toby knows Broom Riding, Conjuring, and Shapechanging. He decides it's time to pick up Spellcasting, so he spends 20 Lil' Points to start at Good (+0) with it.

Skills

Skills are specific things your lil' Wizard knows, or knows how to do. For example, if your Wizard is good at multiplying, adding, dividing, and numbers in general, she probably has the Mathematics Skill.

With a Skill your lil' Wizard has a better chance to succeed with Actions related to the Skill.

Lil' Wizards learn Skills by purchasing them with Lil' Points.

Learn a Skill

When you decide you want your lil' Wizard to know a Skill, just spend 10 Lil' Points, decide what you want her to learn, and write it down on her character sheet.

 * Learn a Skill: 10 LP

Example: Toby wants to learn how to ride a bicycle. He spends 10 Lil' Points and writes down the word "Bicycle" in the Skills area on his character sheet. He could have written "Ride Bike" instead — it's all the same as long as everyone knows what it means.

It's usually best to learn Skills that your lil' Wizard could logically have used in the last Tale or two. For example, after playing "Bewitched Chocolate!" *(see page 70)*, it would make sense to learn Candymaking or Investigating, while Snowboarding and Wilderness Survival are probably not as fitting.

There's no comprehensive list of Skills — practically anything can be a Skill so long as you and the Narrator agree that it makes sense and doesn't apply to too many Actions. As usual, the Narrator has final say about what works as a Skill and what doesn't.

Skill Examples

Here are a few examples of different Skills your lil' Wizard might learn...

Classic Skills: Swimming, Climbing, Running, Jumping, Healing, Mathematics, Geography, History, Hiding, Searching, Juggling, Repairing, Painting, Sewing, Drawing, Cooking...

Wacky Skills: Playing Accordion, Blowing Bubblegum Bubbles, Imitating Birds, Making Funny Faces, Flipping Your Eyelids Inside Out...

Example: After playing the "Lost in Malayak" Tale *(see page 90)*, a lil' Wizard might learn Skiing, Mountain Survival, and Yak Riding.

Note to the Narrator: Picking Skills

Wacky Skills are funny and may help describe a character, but they probably won't come into play very often. You may want to encourage players to start with Classic Skills first, adding Wacky Skills after they've played through a few Tales.

Using a Skill

Using a Skill is almost as easy as learning it. When a character takes an Action related to one of his Skills, the player can reroll the dice if the first roll is a failure. So knowing a Skill gives a lil' Wizard a second chance to succeed.

Example: Estelle has the Acrobatics Skill. She's running through a forest where thick tree roots weave all over the ground. The Narrator decides that she needs to succeed with an Average (7) Body roll to get past the tree roots without tripping. Even with her Better bonus of +1 she only gets a 6, so normally she would trip and fall, maybe bruising her knee or arm in the process. Fortunately she knows Acrobatics! The Narrator decides it's useful in this situation, and so she makes the roll a second time. If her Result is 7 or higher, her Acrobatics Skill keeps her from falling.

Skills aren't just a way to avoid failing — they're a chance to make the Tale more interesting, and to come up with creative solutions to problems facing your lil' Wizard. The best way to use a Skill in the game is to describe an interesting application of your Wizard's knowledge or ability — something that only someone with the Skill could do.

Example: If Estelle scores a Result of 7 or more, she could describe her narrow scrape as some gymnastic move like a somersault. If her description is fun and inventive, and especially if it plays with the idea of a near failure — perhaps something like "I nearly lose my footing but manage to push off one of the roots, roll over a few, and come up beaming at my luck!" — then the Narrator might even award her a Lil' Point.

Be creative with Skills. That's what they're all about!

The Narrator

A lot goes into being the Narrator and it can seem intimidating, but it's actually pretty easy and a whole lot of fun. You get to tell a bigger part of the story, and play a bunch of characters, and help the Tale move forward by deciding when and how the rules are applied. In this chapter we explore the many ways Narrators can make all this happen.

Getting into the Narrator's Shoes

The Narrator has a lot of responsibility in the game. First, he manages the story — describing events, tying in the players' decisions and Actions, and determining the consequences of those decisions and Actions, when they succeed and when they fail. He's the game's referee, both in terms of the rules and the story.

Second, the Narrator knows all the secrets. He already has a sense of what will happen even as the players are still wondering what's going on. Every Tale is like an open-ended novel, in which the start of the story is laid out but the middle and end are left somewhat unde-cided so the lil' Wizards can impact and change what's going on. The Narrator knows the general direction the story is headed in, and what will happen based on the players' most likely choices.

Note to the Narrator: Getting Started

If this is your first time playing Little Wizards, you might find it easiest if the Narrator is the player with the most experience — maybe an adult or a friend who's played before, or the person who's read the most of the book.

You'll probably also find it easiest to play through the three Tales in this book before you make up your own. These three are great examples of what Tales can look like, and should get you started with your own adventures in no time!

* *"Bewitched Chocolate!" has the most guidance for the Narrator, and is written as a basic introduction to the game.*

* *"Lost in Malayak" gives everyone a chance to make up more of the story while still keeping things pretty simple.*

* *"The Squeakydoor Manor Mystery" puts a lot more of the responsibility for the story in the players' hands, with the Narrator reacting to their ideas as the Tale unfolds.*

At the same time, the Narrator is also a player, because it's his responsibility to play the roles of all the characters besides the lil' Wizards. He brings the Tale to life through these other characters, as they interact with the lil' Wizards and introduce their part of the story.

Overall, the Narrator's job is to help the other players and help the Tale so everyone has fun creating the story together. If everyone playing is involved and having fun, the Narrator's done his job splendidly!

Help the Players

There are four main ways to help the players. Each is a little different and they're best used together in whatever order and whenever they come up.

GIVE THEM A HAND!

Help the players have a good time. When a player is struggling to describe his Actions, offer a little encouragement or an idea for him to use. If he's forgotten important information, gently remind him about it.

SURPRISE THEM!

You know all the ins and outs of the story, and all the Tale's secrets. Use that to your advantage and surprise the other players once in a while. The more surprises there are, the more fun the Tale can be.

INVOLVE THEM!

Let the other players speak for themselves and try things out. Let them make mistakes from time to time without penalizing them too harshly. Encourage them to get involved and let them push the Tale forward. They're the heroes of the story, but every hero needs to find her own way!

EMPOWER THEM!

Encourage the other players to use their characters' Powers. Sorcery and Magic are among the best ways to discover Coinworld because they promote imagination and inventive problem solving. Here are a few examples...

+ The lil' Wizards stand at the foot of a very tall brick wall. They could climb over, or they could sail over with Broom Riding.

+ The lil' Wizards need to get through a locked door and they don't have the key. They could give up, but why not use Spellcasting to flip the latch?

+ The lil' Wizards meet a sick boy. They could leave his mother to nurse him back to health with time and care, or they could cure him quickly with Alchemy so they can all go play together!

Help the Tale

Tales are only as special as you make them. There are lots of ways to make them something you and your friends will remember forever. Here are a few examples.

SET THE ATMOSPHERE

It's all about the atmosphere — and we're not talking about the clouds! The other players discover Coinworld through your descriptions, so make sure they're clear and magical!

When you describe a location, remember that vision isn't the lil' Wizards' only sense: describe what they smell in the air, like the fresh scent of roses in a garden or a pleasant perfume worn by a Smiles governess; describe what they feel on their skin and in their hair, like the ruffling of their clothes in a light breeze or the warm touch of the sun on their skin; describe what they hear around them, like a clock tower striking noon or the bleating of livestock being led across a road; and when appropriate, you can even describe what they taste, like refreshing drops of rain as they hold out their tongues in a drizzle.

You can also describe the general feel of locations: they can be happy, disturbing, chilling, and so on. It's really helpful if you have music that fits the atmosphere, or you can just hum a few bars of a tune that sets the mood.

DESCRIBE YOUR CHARACTERS

The many inhabitants of Coinworld — whether they're friendly to the lil' Wizards or not — interact with the other players more than almost any other part of a Tale.

Some of these characters are only around for a short time or don't contribute very much to the story, so you can describe them quickly and simply ("He's an old scholar"). Other characters deserve greater attention, and

Note to the Narrator: Reining It In

While it's a good thing for everyone to pitch in and help direct the story with their Wizards' Actions, some players — especially younger ones — may take things in silly or even ridiculous directions. If they do, try to guide the lil' Wizards toward decisions and Actions that better suit the story and mood of the Tale. Always try to work in the other players' ideas whenever you can, but it's fair to nudge them in helpful directions as well.

First Example: *If a player wants to turn a person into an ice cream cone — an Action that's not only disruptive but also against the rules of magic! — you could suggest that the Wizard instead drop an ice cream cone on the person's head or make it so cold that he feels like an ice cream cone.*

Second Example: *If a player is set on having his favorite animal — a hippopotamus — involved in a Tale that takes place in a busy city with not a lot of room, maybe the adults in the city can ask that the hippo stay in the local zoo. Or perhaps you could suggest an equally unusual but much more manageable critter, like an anteater, and promise to bring the hippo in during a future Tale when there's enough space for him. (Of course, if you make a promise like this be sure to keep it! Consider it a challenge: to come up with a Tale where a hippo can be a star player...)*

the most important characters in a Tale should get the royal treatment, with lots of details for the other players to think about ("He's a very old man with a long white beard, tiny glasses, and a long crooked nose. He's stooped and has a hard time walking, even with his cane").

Descriptions of important characters are always included in published Tales, and unless there's a particular detail that's secret and must be discovered somehow, you shouldn't hesitate to share all this information with the other players.

You can also impersonate a character's voice when you speak as them (the old man probably has a quivering voice, for example), or you can mime his gestures (maybe he uses his hands when he speaks, or chews gum, or scratches his head a lot).

MIME YOUR ACTIONS

Body language can say just as much as a long and detailed description, sometimes even more. Let's say a character has an unusual walk... Try it yourself! Wave your hands around to indicate that a character is frantic or scared. Motion your arms up and down to show the ground's movement during an earthquake. Beat your chest when playing a gorilla. Mimed scenes are a great way to get everyone involved in a more than intellectual way. It's also a great way to get a laugh!

MAKE THE WORLD YOUR OWN

Coinworld is what you make of it. You don't have to follow any Tale exactly; you can change the parts you don't like, adding characters, moving the action to a different location, or even switching up the ending if you want. Once you know Coinworld well enough you'll certainly want to create your own Tales but until then, change the ones you have! Make the world yours, and it will be more believable and fun for everyone.

The Three Laws of the Narrator

Ultimately there are three laws for every Narrator...

1. BE CONFIDENT AND FAIR

Players will have all kinds of ideas about what their Wizards might do, and the Basic Rules should cover most situations and Actions (*see page 39*). When you're unsure and the rules don't help, just make the decision that seems the most fair and keep the game moving. A little discussion is fine but don't let the game slow to a standstill over it. Remember that you can always change your mind later, and make another call the next time the situation or Action comes up.

2. SET THE GROUND RULES

As the Narrator you set the limits for the Wizards, and decide what's possible and what's not. This is especially true when it comes to Magic and Sorcery. Without limits Coinworld quickly becomes a crazy place, with elephants floating through the sky, oceans made of pudding, and forests dripping with candy canes. Maybe that's the world everyone wants to play in, and if so that's great! If not, don't hesitate to set the ground rules to make sure the limits of magic are understood by everyone who's playing. In this case the most important thing is to stay consistent.

3. IMPROVISE

Sometimes players will do things you never could have predicted. They'll decide to search areas you haven't detailed or talk to characters who aren't supposed to be big parts of the story. They'll even decide the story is about something else entirely! In these situations it's best to roll with it and let the players and their Wizards guide the story for a while. Let them describe what's happening, and make things up to match. Maybe you'll find a way to bring it back to the Tale you started, or maybe you'll wind up telling a whole new Tale! Either outcome is fine, so long as everyone has fun.

4. CHEAT!

You thought there were only three rules? There's a secret fourth rule — you can cheat! When necessary, you can bend or even break the rules to make sure a story doesn't go completely off the rails. You'll know when this happens: it will start to feel like a bad movie or book, or the bad guys will start winning, or you'll notice that no one is having any fun. In any of these situations you're well within your rights to roll in secret (saying the dice came up whatever you want), or to change the Tale, or whatever, so long as you're doing it for the good of the whole game.

Little Wizard Tales

You explore Coinworld by playing through adventures, which are called "Tales." These are often planned ahead of time but sometimes decided as you play. When a Tale is prepared, the Narrator makes up the beginning of the story, including something interesting for the lil' Wizards to investigate, or something for them to do. The rest of the Tale is outlined, with an idea of what may happen if the Wizards make certain choices.

You can get started with the three Tales in this book. They can be played in any order, though they're presented from most introductory to most advanced, so first-time Narrators and players may want to go through them in the order they're provided.

In "Bewitched Chocolate!" *(see page 70)*, the lil' Wizards solve a fairly straightforward mystery in the town of Ellys on the Smiles Archipelago. There's plenty of opportunity for the Wizards to find their own way and discover what's happening on their own terms, and guidance is provided for players and Narrators new to the game.

"Lost in Malayak" *(see page 90)* takes the lil' Wizards to the snowy rises of a mountain chain deep in the middle of the Steppes Archipelago. There they search for the totem yak of the Ermine Tribe, which has recently gone missing. This is a slightly more advanced Tale, in which the Narrator is expected to embellish and improvise the setting and people of Steppes, and the players are confronted with a couple of simple but open-ended problems to solve. Significant support is provided before the Tale, in a chapter entirely dedicated to describing Steppes for traveling Wizards.

Finally, "The Squeakydoor Manor Mystery" *(see page 109)* has the lil' Wizards visiting a strange estate on the Shivers Archipelago. They're asked to find all the pieces of a Medallion, and they may choose the order and methods of doing so. This Tale is much more freeform than the other two and requires the Narrator to know the setting and characters well before the Tale begins so he can guide the players' investigation.

This third Tale is preceded by a chapter detailing the Shivers Archipelago. Like the chapter on Steppes, this includes a description of the location's main islands, a short overview of the inhabitants and their culture, and details about local animals, plants, and oddities — just what you need to describe the lil' Wizards' adventures!

Additional Tale seeds are sprinkled throughout. A Tale seed is an idea, an inspiration for the Narrator that you can turn into a full-blown story of your very own.

Have a wonderful game in Coinworld!

The Tales

Each *Little Wizards* Tale is broken down like this...

+ **Summary:** This section quickly sums up the Tale, giving an overview of what might happen and how the players can explore and discover. Characters and locations are sometimes described here as well. The Summary includes the Tale's plot and secrets, so the Narrator needs to keep it secret, at least at the start.

+ **The Tale, sometimes divided into chapters:** Tales commonly unfold like books, with the lil' Wizards moving from one chapter to the next as they push deeper into the story. Sometimes the Wizards will be able to move back and forth between chapters, and other times entering a new chapter leaves the old ones behind for good. Each chapter also contains rules the Narrator might need to resolve special or important Actions.

+ **The Ending:** The end of a Tale is never really known until the Narrator and players decide what it is, but each of the Tales in this book includes information that can be helpful in guiding things to a satisfactory conclusion. This is especially true in an investigation like "The Squeakydoor Manor Mystery" (*see page 109*), in which reaching the end of the Tale depends on the Wizards learning the truth of what's going on. Sometimes a Tale will offer ways that the adventure can continue. Each of the Tales in this book can lead into the next, letting you play through them in order, one after another.

A Tale: Bewitched Chocolate!

Warning: This chapter is for the Narrator's eyes only. Players — move along now or you'll spoil your fun!

Note: Throughout the Tales in this book, you'll find boxes titled "Read to the Players." You can read these aloud if you're having a hard time describing situations. It's a great little shortcut!

Summary

Since the beginning of the week, something odd has been happening in the city of Ellys, on the Smiles Archipelago. Several seemingly unrelated people are acting very strangely!

A new brand of chocolate is behind all this craziness. Less than a month ago, a chocolate factory named Ellys Delicacies opened for business a few miles outside the city. There's a problem, though — a band of greedy brownies that lives nearby decided to have a little fun. They took over the factory and kidnapped Mr. Cocoa, the chocolate maker and owner of the factory.

The brownies have tampered with the machinery so it keeps making chocolate on its own. They also added Brownie Joke Powder to the chocolate recipe. This is what's causing all the bizarre behavior — in everyone who eats the chocolate!

The brownies are holding Mr. Cocoa prisoner at their camp in a forest clearing near the factory. They aren't hurting him, but they tease him and play practical jokes on the poor man all day long.

Locations & Characters

Here's a little more information about the people and places in this Tale. Use these details to describe the city and important characters as the lil' Wizards encounter them.

LOCATION: ELLYS

This city is located on Curve's End (a region at the north of the Smiles Archipelago). It's one of the most pleasant destinations on Heads.

Cute white cottages stand close by the ocean and a gentle wind from the east blows gently over them every day. The sun shines brightly over this nice quiet town almost all year round. The weather and idyllic scenery are two of the main reasons this is such a popular vacation spot.

Ellys is famous for its sweets — delightful chocolates, bonbons, and pastries. On weekends, many residents stroll along the Trail of Sweets. This wonderful walk starts at Confectioner's Square (downtown) and then follows the town wall overlooking the beach, where vendors sell every kind of candy there is.

CHARACTER: MR. COCOA

Mr. Cocoa owns and runs the Ellys Delicacies factory. He's short and pot-bellied, with a wide nose and bright eyes. He often fiddles with his bushy gray mustache. This gentle man has always dreamed of becoming a chocolate maker, but he may regret his choice if the lil' Wizards don't come to his rescue!

CHARACTERS: THE BROWNIES

There are eight of these tiny humanoids, each about a foot tall. They have large pointy ears, small beady black eyes, and very long pointy noses. They wear tunics and caps made out of woven leaves, and shoes made out of tree bark.

The brownies spend most of their time using magic to play jokes on humans and animals. They're tremendously greedy and have turned Mr. Cocoa's chocolate factory into their new playground.

Chapter 1: Strange Occurrences

First the players should introduce their characters, especially if this is the first time they're playing together. After that, your job as the Narrator is to get the players involved in the story. Describe the scene and, if necessary, give the players an idea of which direction to go.

If you aren't sure how to start after the lil' Wizards are described, read this to them...

Read to the Players

Spring has been enjoyable and warm. This time of year, many residents of Ellys City relax in local parks and gardens, enjoying the gentle breezes of the Smiles Archipelago.

This year things are a little different, though. Starting about a week ago, a wind of craziness seems to have blown over the inhabitants of the coastal city...

Continued on next page...

A baker was seen swimming in the fountain at the center of Confectioner's Square — with all his clothes on. Even his apron!

A mother has been happily cruising around town — in her son's stroller!

Some teenagers have been acting like little children, throwing tantrums and not listening to their parents. You're more grown up than that!

Just yesterday an old lady was out shopping, and she was dressed like Santa Claus!

Doctors have no explanation. The police have no clue what to do. The firemen are afraid an accident may happen. No one knows what's going on, but one thing's for sure — this isn't natural!

....

After hearing of these curious events, the lil' Wizards will probably want to investigate. Encourage them to do so, and let them choose where to start.

The baker is easy to find. In fact, he's currently swimming in the public fountain ("The water's lovely! Come on in!"). If the players talk with him, they learn that he's discovered a new chocolate that he intends to use for his pastries. Of course, he's tasted this new chocolate and he's crazy about it.

The mother is also easy to spot since she's riding her stroller all through town. She's more interested in her stroller than the Wizards ("Wow, check out that hill! Dare you to race me!"), but the characters notice a smear of chocolate around her mouth.

The teenagers, two boys and a girl, are at a local playground. They're playing on the swings and monkey bars. Each of them is thirteen or fourteen, but speaks like a toddler ("Wanna play wiff us? The swing goes up to the sky!"). Chocolate bars stick out of their pockets, but they don't want to share. In fact, they pitch fits if the lil' Wizards ask for a piece.

What if the lil' Wizards eat the Chocolate?

If a lil' Wizard eats the chocolate funny things are bound to happen. However, unlike regular people, the Wizards' behavior doesn't change; instead their Powers go haywire! Or their appearance changes, or something else happens.

Maybe a Wizard's hair changes color, or his voice gets really high or low. Maybe his Divination suddenly reveals things like a vintage movie. Any hilarious idea will work!

In fact, your players may have some great ideas of their own — ask them what happens when they eat the chocolate, maybe after you've described what happens to the first of them who takes a bite (and remember, you can always say no to any idea that's too crazy or may disrupt the game).

The old lady only leaves home to go shopping. She's a bit deaf and constantly asks the lil' Wizards to speak up ("What's that? I can't hear you!"). She goes shopping early in the morning every day ("I buy bread, some milk, kibbles for my cat Mr. Meow, and a little bit of chocolate...").

After these encounters, the players probably realize the chocolate has something to do with all this craziness, but if they don't you might want to introduce some other characters who are acting weird and have them mention chocolate, or have chocolate on them.

When the players ask where the affected people got their chocolate, they learn that a new factory has opened up: Ellys Delicacies.

A van from the factory delivers chocolate bars very early every Monday to all the sweet shops in town. The shop owners place orders with the drivers, and no one has ever visited the factory, or even knows where it is! (The people of Ellys are very trusting, and also prefer to keep things simple and easy whenever they can.)

Chapter 2: Chocolate Delivery

This chapter assumes the lil' Wizards wait for the delivery van to come, on Monday at dawn. You can give them a hand by suggesting they shouldn't miss this opportunity. If they still do, maybe the factory starts making more chocolate than usual — another suggestion that something weird is going on — and the delivery vans start arriving on other days as well, now with even more chocolate the stores haven't ordered!

When the lil' Wizards follow the van you can either read the following or make up your own description to get things started...

....

Read to the Players

The sun is just coming up over Ellys. A light fog slowly moves through the cool and calm streets.

A van drives merrily along the cobblestone street. "Ellys Delicacies, Original Chocolate" is painted on its sides. The van stops in front of a candy store, its engine still running.

After a few moments, the van moves on, leaving three boxes in front of the store's door.

....

The boxes are full of chocolate bars. Anyone who is really observant may notice a whiff of pine needles (*see page 75 for more on observant characters*).

The van looks normal at first glance, but a closer inspection or successful use of Divination — an Average (7) Action — shows that something magical is going on with it. Without Divination a Wizard looking inside the van only guesses that something's wrong, while successful use of Divination reveals that the van is somehow driving itself and the driver is nothing more than an illusion!

Following the Van

All lil' Wizards have the Broom Riding Power, so they can all follow the van from a distance on their flying brooms. There are two steps, each involving an Action, and in each step there's a chance for one or more Wizards to fall behind, get lost, or find other trouble on the way to the Ellys Factory.

The first step is for the lil' Wizards following the van to the edge of the city, and the second step is for them following the van through the countryside until it arrives at the factory.

As explained in the Basic Rules, an Action is resolved with a die roll (see page 39). This means each player will roll once for each of the two steps.

Note to the Narrator: Observant Characters

Which lil' Wizards are "observant"?

* *An observant character might be the Wizard whose player says she's looking around to see if she spots anything interesting or out of place.*

* *An observant character might be a Wizard who succeeds with a Brain roll. The Difficulty of this kind of Action is based on the situation and on how critical the clue is to the Tale. If the players really need to discover something for the Tale to move forward, keep the Difficulty of finding or noticing it low.*

* *When it's absolutely essential that the lil' Wizards find or notice something, the Wizard who's looking the hardest, or the one with the highest Brain can simply find or notice it. Don't let the dice throw off the story!*

If you have only one player in your game, her Wizard is automatically observant.

* A Wizard with a Good (+0) Broom Riding Power needs a 5 or higher to succeed.

* A Wizard with a Better (+1) Broom Riding Power needs a 4 or higher to succeed.

* A Wizard with a Best (+2) Broom Riding Power needs a 3 or higher to succeed.

With a Success, the Wizard follows the van without any problem.

With a Brilliant Success, the Wizard follows the van with ease, and even performs some acrobatics to show off a bit!

With a Failure, the Wizard has a hard time keeping up with the van; he's falling behind and has to work a little harder but eventually makes it. He might be a bit tired, though!

With a Disaster, the Wizard rams into an obstacle (a streetlight, a street sign, or a parked car). He isn't injured but his friends will certainly tease him when he catches up!

STEP 2:
FOLLOWING THE VAN ON THE COUNTRY ROAD

The van picks up speed once it leaves Ellys, as it no longer has to make any stops to deliver boxes in town. At this point the Difficulty of keeping up rises to Average (7)...

STEP 1:
FOLLOWING THE VAN IN THE CITY

The van stops frequently while it's in the city, so the Difficulty to keep up with it is Very Easy (5)...

Note to the Narrator: Describing Failure

This chapter's two Actions are set up so the lil' Wizards can't actually fail. When they roll a Failure, or even a Disaster, they simply fall behind a bit and maybe take a tumble or embarrass themselves a little before they catch up. What if you want the chance for an Action to actually fail, though? In this situation it's a little tricky, as the Wizards have to make it to the factory for the Tale to continue.

Here are some options for these particular Actions as examples of what's possible with Actions in your own Tales...

+ The first time a Wizard fails, especially if it was a really low roll, let the player reroll at a higher Difficulty to reflect trying to fly faster and make up lost ground. That Very Easy (5) Action is now Easy (6)!

+ If the Wizard fails again, or you just want a different option, think about what failing means. It's simple to say the Wizard gets lost, but it means that you have to keep track of Wizards in two places, and it could throw the Tale off course. Instead, maybe the other Wizards arrive first and can take an Action before their momentarily lost friend arrives.

+ If all the players fail, perhaps they lose track of the van and need to figure out a new way to get to the factory. Maybe they hear giggles in the woods and find a trail left by the brownies, which leads to the factory, or perhaps they meet someone by the road or in a nearby forest who has seen strange creatures at the factory.

+ Don't forget that familiars and other characters can help! The rules for Teamwork are on page 43.

The most important thing to remember is that failing an Action should add new challenges, complications, or comedy. Failure shouldn't stop the Tale or be no fun for the players and the Narrator. If failure with an Action will absolutely throw the Tale off, consider skipping that Action and instead letting the lil' Wizards succeed just by describing what they do.

+ A Wizard with a Good (+0) Broom Riding Power needs a 7 or higher to succeed.

+ A Wizard with a Better (+1) Broom Riding Power needs a 6 or higher to succeed.

+ A Wizard with a Best (+2) Broom Riding Power needs a 5 or higher to succeed.

With a Success, the Wizard keeps the van in sight the whole way to the factory.

With a Brilliant Success, the Wizard not only keeps the van in sight but can so something else at the same time! (If no one used Divination to learn that the van is being magically driven, she can do that now.)

With a Failure, the Wizard loses sight of the van once or twice, but *eventually* makes it to the factory — perhaps with the help (and teasing) of her friends.

With a Disaster, the Wizard is distracted by a passing bird and almost runs into the van. So much for the element of surprise!

WHAT IF THE LIL' WIZARDS DON'T USE THEIR BROOMSTICKS?

Maybe they walk or ride bicycles or horses. Maybe they "borrow" a car (assuming one of them knows how to drive!). In any of these cases, use the same two steps for following the van, replacing the Broom Riding Power with the Brain Trait. All the Difficulties and story outcomes stay the same.

Warning! In Coinworld, just like in our world, only adults are allowed to drive. If the lil' Wizards "borrow" a vehicle and someone sees them, they'll be in trouble!

Chapter 3: Big Trouble at the Chocolate Factory

Finally, the van arrives at a newly built and fairly small factory at the end of the road, close to a dense forest. The vehicle pulls into a small garage and the door closes behind it.

Read to the Players

You've arrived at a factory at the edge of a forest. The sign above the gate reads "Ellys Delicacies." A warm wind tickles your nostrils with the irresistible smell of chocolate. It's so sweet and yummy!

The lil' Wizards can walk or fly all the way around the factory. There are no grates or vents, but there are three doors...

The Main Door

This factory's front door is locked. A lil' Mage or lil' Sorcerer can try to unlock it with the Spellcasting Power — it's an Average (7) Difficulty roll. Conjuring a key that unlocks any door is Almost Impossible (10). If either Action succeeds, the door magically opens and the lil' Wizards can enter the lobby. If not, the door stays locked. Fortunately, there are a couple other doors into the building...

The Brownies' Powder

The brownies have dumped this magic powder in the mixing trough. The lil' Wizards can use Divination to tell it's magic — it's an Average (7) roll — but they can't tell what it does.

A character who eats some of the powder is affected as if they ate the chocolate. It interacts with his magic and makes something strange or funny happen. Maybe soap bubbles come out of his mouth when he speaks, or his skin becomes pink with green polka dots...

The effects are temporary and last a day at most.

The Garage Door

This wide metal door slides vertically, rolling up over the entrance. It's locked too, and just like the main door it can be opened with magic: it's an Average (7) Spellcasting roll.

The garage door can also be forced open by hand; any lil' Wizards who are feeling strong can try to lift it and crawl under. This is a Hard (8) Body Action. Up to three characters can work together on this, in which case the Teamwork rules are used. The character with the highest Body makes the roll and one or two other characters (or familiars) can add +1 each.

Anyone who goes through this door enters the garage (see page 79).

The Service Door

Around the back of the building is a service door. It is unlocked and leads directly to the factory's machine room, where the chocolate is prepared and packed.

An observant character notices a chocolate bar wrapper next to this door, not far from the forest edge.

Read to the Players

As soon as you get inside the factory, you can hear the racket of machinery hard at work. The smell of chocolate is stronger and your mouth starts to water...

Inside the Factory

You don't need a map for a building this simple. Once the lil' Wizards are inside, they can move around from one room to another as they want.

THE LOBBY

This small room is almost empty. There's a plant in the corner and on the wall is a large painting of Ellys as seen from the ocean. There are three unlocked doors. One leads to Mr. Cocoa's office, another to the machine room, and the last one leads to the garage.

THE OFFICE

Mr. Cocoa's office is a large space, decorated with plants and framed pictures. The largest picture is of Mr. Cocoa in front of this factory at its grand opening. It's dated about three months ago.

There's a lot of boring paperwork here — invoices, purchasing orders, and various notes — but instead of it being in neat piles it's spread all over the floor, mixed with lots of pine needles. All the windows are closed, so a wind couldn't have caused this mess...

THE GARAGE

This room smells funny — like chocolate mixed with engine grease (gross!). A set of tools is meticulously sorted on a workshop table along the wall, obviously used to repair and maintain the factory's machines and the van.

The van is parked here and its driver's seat is empty (no surprise to anyone who succeeded with a Divination Action earlier).

A conveyor belt chugs along in the corner, delivering box after box of freshly packed chocolate bars. The boxes pile up, one after another, with no one to collect them.

THE MACHINE ROOM

This enormous room takes up most of the factory's interior. It's filled with machines and... noise! Conveyor belts run through the whole room, moving hundreds of chocolate bars through the process from being poured to being wrapped for stores.

There are two locations inside the machine room...

The Cold Room

This huge and very chilly walk-in fridge contains shelves of ingredients used to make the chocolate: cocoa, sugar, and milk. Lil' Wizards who enter might want to Conjure a sweater!

The Production Line

Most of the machine room is taken up by a massive production line where ingredients are mixed. It starts with an enormous mechanical mixing trough, and then the chocolate is sent to the molding line where it's poured into solid bars. Finally, the bars are wrapped and packed into boxes, and these boxes are whisked away to the garage on a conveyor belt.

All the machines are running: the mixer is blending ingredients; the chocolate is being poured into molds, and it's being wrapped and packed into boxes. Oddly, there are no workers here. No one is minding the machines, and as boxes come off the conveyor belt in the garage they're just piling up there.

Observant characters (*see page 75*) notice a strange colored powder on the inside of the mixing trough. It shines in the light and smells like fresh pine sap.

Chapter 4: Call of the Forest

The answer to the mystery is close, in the forest behind the factory. There are several ways the characters can discover this...

+ They find the pine needles in Mr. Cocoa's office (or remember the scent of pine needles in the chocolate boxes)

+ They find the magic powder (it smells of pine sap)

+ They follow the chocolate wrappers behind the factory, which lead to the forest... Behind the factory, close to the service door, the characters can find an empty chocolate bar wrapper. A character approaching it notices there's another one a few feet from the first, closer to the forest's edge, and then another a little deeper into the woods...

Read to the Players

As you enter the forest a faint smell of sap tickles your nose, and you realize there are no birds chipping, or animals moving about. Something is wrong here.

Suddenly you hear noises: a tiny high-pitched laugh followed by a low-pitched complaint.

Approaching the sounds, you see an old tree in a clearing. A heavy man with big bushy eyebrows and a white mustache is tied up to the tree trunk and brownies laugh and dance around him.

The brownies have taken his shoes and socks and are having fun tickling his feet with feathers. The man is crying and laughing at the same time, and he begs them to stop.

The Joker Brownies

The players may ask about brownies, and this is an excellent chance for them to test their Brains! Have anyone who asks make either a Brain or Divination roll at Very Easy (5) Difficulty. Each lil' Wizard who succeeds knows one of the following facts about the tricky little creatures. A Brilliant Success provides two of these facts...

+ Brownies aren't mean so much as mischievous. They really like practical jokes.

+ They love sweets and fresh fruit.

+ When they aren't playing tricks, they nap. They sleep *a lot.*

+ Brownies aren't very brave. For example, they hide like rabbits as soon as they hear a storm coming!

What Do You Do?

It's time to make a plan! If the players need some help coming up with ideas, here are a few possibilities...

WAIT FOR THE BROWNIES TO FALL ASLEEP

Eventually the brownies grow bored of tickling Mr. Cocoa and fall asleep around him. At that point one or more of the lil' Wizards could try to sneak past them with an Average (7) Brain roll. Success finds the quiet path, while failure snaps a twig and wakes the brownies!

Untying Mr. Cocoa is an Easy (6) Body roll. This can be rerolled at Average (7), then Hard (8), and so on, and up to three lil' Wizards can work together to get him free.

Of course the lil' Wizards might think of a way to use magic for these rolls instead.

Failing the sneak roll, or failing too many rolls to untie Mr. Cocoa rouses the brownies, and the Wizards must switch to another plan — maybe one of the other two here...

NEGOTIATE WITH THE BROWNIES

The brownies aren't about to let their prisoner go without something in return. The lil' Wizards need something to offer the brownies, like fruit juice, candy, or a cheesecake (they like sweets, remember?). Maybe one of the Wizards brought a treat, or one of them can use Conjuring to make one.

So long as it's something the brownies actually want, they're happy to trade. They were getting bored of Mr. Cocoa and his factory anyway! The exchange is still a little tense: the brownies form a circle and discuss the offer in a hushed whisper for several long moments before they make their decision.

SCARE THE BROWNIES AWAY

The brownies are skittish and easily scared by the sound of thunder (or any frightening noise, really). They also flee if genuinely threatened in any way — say, by turning a forest plant into a brownie-eating monster!

Magic and Sorcery are equally useful here. The Difficulty of the Spellcasting roll is up to the Narrator and based on how the Wizards want to scare the brownies. For example, calling a thunderclap or two is Easy (6), while a lightning bolt striking in the clearing is Average (7). Turning a plant into that brownie-eating monster is Very Hard (9)!

Success with any of these Actions, or another Action the Narrator thinks will spook the brownies, causes them to scatter and flee into the forest. This is a great chance for the players to be creative!

Epilogue

Once freed, Mr. Cocoa embraces the lil' Wizards ("Thank you so much, children! I was starting to think I'd spend the rest of my life tied to this trunk, at the mercy of those dreadful creatures!"). He offers to send them a box of his best chocolate every month for a whole year! If the lil' Wizards love chocolate, they're in for a treat!

Back in town, everything returns to normal as the effects of the brownie powder wear off and Mr. Cocoa cleans up his factory. Within a few days, or perhaps a week, all the craziness is forgotten.

What about the brownies? Well, they had their fun and they're done for now. It won't take them long to find something new to do, and before long they'll forget the chocolate factory and their captive. Who knows? Maybe they will meet the lil' Wizards again, in another *Little Wizards* Tale...

Note to the Narrator: Don't Forget to Award Lil' Points!

It's the end of the Tale and if you haven't already awarded the lil' Wizards some Lil' Points, you should do that now (see page 57 for guidelines).

Don't forget to award some just for getting to the end of the Tale, and be especially generous to those who came up with and participated in any unique or creative ways to deal with the brownies.

Especially in their first adventure, the lil' Wizards should earn enough Lil' Points to make at least one improvement. Everyone likes to see their characters grow, and maybe their new ability will help them in their next Tale! At the very least it will give you something to talk about next...

The Steppes Archipelago

"There's little as enchanting as the sight of the Malayak dominating the Steppes Archipelago from its snowy heights." — Gideon Herasmus, tireless traveler

Steppes is the northernmost archipelago on Heads, and also the coldest. Its population is mostly made up of nomadic tribes who travel all year round across the tall vistas and lower slopes of its towering, snowy mountains.

There are four main islands in Steppes: **Malayak** (the largest), **Kashia**, **Kriska**, and **Yukin**. The people who live here are called the "Steppish," and their language has the same name. Their currency is called the Yak (10 Naks make one Yak), but they often trade goods and services instead of using the coins.

Malayak

Malayak stretches across the northern edge of Heads. The island would be totally flat if not for the mountain chain across its full length, separating the cold southern side from the very, *very* cold northern side. Plains extend from both sides of the mountain range. They're covered with small trees and thorny bushes, and they're home to huge **herds of yaks**. These animals are special to the locals, and treated as well as any person.

The peaks of the Malayak Mountains are lost in the clouds. This doesn't mean they're extremely high — on Coinworld, clouds are fairly low. Still, Malayak boasts the tallest summits on Heads. Fortunately for the nomads and the yak herds, the Malayak Mountains have many passes crossing from one side to the other. **Snow monkeys** make their homes in the snowy peaks, and **azure eagles** soar through the skies overhead.

There are three main cities on Malayak — **Baator**, **Kinuite**, and **Oglii** — all on the south side of the island where the temperature isn't as severe and the archipelago has regular contact with the other cultures of Heads.

Baator is the largest and busiest of the three cities, a southeastern harbor bustling with energy, noise, and exotic smells. In this port you can sell wool, coal, and ore, and buy all sorts of resources that can't be found anywhere on Steppes, including fruits, grains, and manufactured items. Baator also has a museum of Steppish culture, its rooms and collections spanning the history and the archipelago's civilization. The Baator museum doesn't hold a candle to the sprawling collections on Keys, but it offers an excellent chance to learn some of the local culture, not to mention stay warm!

Kinuite is located along the northwestern curve of the **White Peninsula**, beyond the **White Cabaniers Forest**. Kinuite is an important location in Steppish folklore, and its economy. The wooden architecture here distinguishes the community from any other in the area, and the craftsmen have access to a large quantity of wood, which they carve into many useful objects sold across Heads.

The local Sky Festival celebrates the end of winter. For two days and nights, citizens move all of their furniture outdoors and go about their daily life beneath the warming (yet still rather frosty) northern sky.

Olgii lies at the far west end of the island. It's a small community, lost at the very end of Steppes and facing the ocean's vastness alone. It's also a mandatory stop for nomads bringing news from the rest of the archipelago.

A note for the gourmets: Olgii's salmon is a delight!

Yukin

Yukin is barely visible, tucked beyond the northwestern curve of Malayak, at the very edge of Coinworld. This small island is snowed in all year round, to the great delight of its inhabitants and the tourists who come to admire its white-blanketed landscapes. Of course, there's no snow without cold, so hats, scarves, and mittens are absolute necessities.

Tale Seed: The Great White Yak

Storytellers in Steppes claim that seeing the legendary Great White Yak is the best possible omen for a nomadic tribe. Following its tracks is said to lead to a secret location called the Frozen Rift. No human has ever set foot in this mysterious place, which supposedly hides unexpected treasures from the outside world.

Every year the small town of **Niska** organizes a great ice sculpting competition. This event gathers all of Steppes' artists (and even a few invited from elsewhere) to put their imagination, talent, and skill to the test, and amaze spectators with the short-lived beauty of their creations. Blocks of ice of all sizes are drilled, cut, sawed, heated, melted, and polished to create the boldest and most original shapes on display. Sorcerers and Mages can participate, but using Powers is strictly forbidden!

Kashia & Kriska

East of Malayak are two ice floes named Kashia and Kriska. Their sizes shift with the seasons, and they don't have any permanent residents because their climate is so hostile. Sea lions, seals, walruses, and even a few white bears live there, however, having an easier time with the extreme weather.

Kashia shelters a mysterious location; at the heart of the island, a **grotto** cuts into an ice hill. Inside, there's a 15-foot tall ice statue shaped like a yak. No one knows who sculpted it or when it was made. One thing is certain: there's magic in the place that keeps the statue from melting. All the nomad tribes travel to Kashia once a year. They cross over to the island on rowboats to pay tribute to the sacred statue.

Kriska has fewer visitors, and the animals living there are fine with that. A few Steppish people visit to gather **whistling snowdrops**, the only plants that can grow on ice.

Living on Steppes

People on Steppes primarily earn a living by ranching, making clothes (in wool and leather), and sometimes farming. Trading is very common between the tribes,

though the coastal cities also use money, mainly to trade with visitors from other archipelagos.

Steppes cities are independent and led by elected leaders, while the rest of the land is public property (the Steppish people often say that "beyond each city's limits, the land belongs to all"). Tribes are led by chiefs, elected by the elders of the tribe's clans. Within each tribe, the chief and elders form a council that maintains their ancient laws and customs, and make important decisions for the group.

There are no schools in Steppes' great wilderness; each community educates its own children. In the cities, workers and craftspeople sometimes take apprentices, but most often these spots are reserved for their own children. A few teachers travel with the clans, bringing their knowledge to the remote wilds. Some tutors specialize in teaching magic to those with the ability.

The Steppes island dwellers maintain an oral tradition dating back to the dawn of time. Storytellers are as respected as Sorcerers and Mages, and there's always room for them at a family table or close to a campfire. Singing is also highly cherished; people sing during marches, while herding yaks, and to entertain travelers. There is, however, an odd tone to Steppish songs that outsiders often find difficult to appreciate.

Yaks have a very important place in Steppish culture. Several annual festivals are dedicated to them and they're at the center of many local pastimes, such as yak pack races and yak training tournaments.

Nomadic Tribes

Steppish culture places huge importance on the tribal structure. More than half the Steppish people are nomads who travel across the archipelago all year round. Every tribe moves with a herd of yaks, and the animals are respected as much as humans.

Each tribe has a guardian yak that serves as the tribe's symbol. The guardian yak leads the tribe's way and the nomads generally trust its wisdom and instincts. A tribe's guardian yak also approves the candidates for chief. Each of these special animals has decorated horns and a mane and tail braided with threads matching the tribe's colors. The tribe's children care for the guardian yak's coat, brushing it every day and trimming it as needed. This wool is then used to make clothes for newborn tribe members.

Nomads traditionally live in yurts. These are large circular tents built out of stretched hides and fastened to a wooden frame with ropes. Even the most sedentary Steppish people prefer them to brick or stone buildings because yurts are easy to take down and move. It's nice to be able to pick up and move whenever you like — and not just the furniture!

Magic on Steppes

Magic is discreet on Steppes, though not for lack of talent, or due to bad reputation. Magic is only used in times of great need, not on a daily basis as it is most everywhere else. The people of Steppes face a difficult climate, and they enjoy a simple and natural way of life.

A Few Steppish Phrases:

- **Hi!:** *"Sanbainayu"*
- **Goodbye:** *"Untaraille"*
- **Thank you:** *"Bayarlala"*
- **How cold!:** *"Bri glaglak"*

Most Sorcerers have adapted to this mindset, and it's not uncommon for them to do almost everything by hand, falling back on magic only when they absolutely must.

Due to the lack to a strong educational structure and the cultural tendency to avoid magic unless it's needed, Mages tend to be rare on Steppes.

When Steppish Wizards inevitably crave adventure, they pull on their boots and travel. Sometimes they join a nomadic tribe, and the community is more than happy to welcome them. Wizards are, after all, rather handy!

The main keepers of Steppish oral tradition are called **Ancients**, and they're the best spoken and most widely traveled of all Wizards on Steppes. They're exceptional storytellers, and celebrated everywhere they go. One such living legend is Berenicia, an endearing character who's fully developed and ready for play on page 87.

Weird Object: Yakurt

Yakurt is a magic culinary specialty made of whipped fermented yak milk. This creamy dairy product is prepared by Sorcerers and poured into a round leather container, then served frozen. Its properties go beyond its striking taste — Yakurt protects against frostbite and colds!

One final note about magic on Steppes: Broom Riding isn't easy here. Snow and wind make flight conditions very difficult. Young Sorcerers and Mages need to be extremely cautious when in the air, lest they wind back up on the ground — often with a few more bruises to show for their trouble.

Someone to Meet

Here's a character the lil' Wizards might meet on the Steppes Archipelago...

Berenicia, Ancient Nomad Storyteller

Berenicia is the oldest Sorcerer on Steppes — or at least, that's what all the stories say. Her wrinkled face is framed with abundant snow-white hair, and she's always dressed mainly in black. She lives a solitary life but sometimes joins a tribe for a short time. In these moments she's seemingly always found near a roaring campfire, sharing clever stories of wonderful places she's been and even more wonderful people she's met.

Like all Wizards, Berenicia is never quite alone. Her familiar is a huge black yak named "Coal," whom she rides wherever she goes (Berenicia has never been completely comfortable flying on a broomstick).

HER TRAITS
Body: Better (+1)
Heart: Best (+2)
Brain: Best (+2)

HER POWERS
Broom Riding: Good (+0)
Spellcasting: Best (+2)
Divination: Best (+2)

HER BELONGINGS

A cookbook as old as the first snow, its pages faded by time
An enchanted yurt that builds itself up and breaks itself down
A very comfortable travel saddle

HER FAMILIAR

Coal, a huge, very smart, and very grumpy black yak

Animals and Plants

Steppes is home to many interesting creatures...

Yaks

The yak is a large mammal found exclusively on Steppes (at least on Coinworld). Its very thick coat protects it from extreme cold and grows in a variety of colors. A yak has two large jutting horns. Its sight is quite poor but it makes up for this handicap with excellent smell and hearing. The people of Steppes use yaks as mounts and draft animals. They also use the animal's wool for yarn and clothing.

Snow Monkeys

These playful primates inhabit the high plains of the Malayak Mountains. Nature provided them with thick white fur, making them invisible to the untrained eye against a snowy backdrop. Snow monkeys are widely known to be extremely gentle, and many Steppes tribes tell stories about the animals helping them cross a fissure or leading them to shelter in a storm. A few tribes even claim that snow monkeys share their food with humans.

Azure Eagles

The sky over Steppes belongs to the azure eagles —
giant raptors with blue feathers. These creatures are for-
midable predators and feed on the archipelago's rodents.
They're featured in many stories and their feathers
adorn many pointy hats owned by Steppes Wizards.

Whistling Snowdrops

These strange plants only grow on unstable terrain
near cliffs and ravines, and so they're a good warning
sign of potential danger for travelers and animals. The
whistling snowdrops play a low but piercing tone when
approached, which strengthens to an earsplitting shriek
as the intruder closes in. Whistling snowdrops are a
component of several alchemical concoctions common
in Steppes.

Cabin Trees

Cabin trees are the most common trees on Steppes.
Their long, thick branches intertwine with those of
other nearby cabin trees, forming a thick canopy that
offers excellent shelter against wind and rain.

A Tale: Lost in Malayak

Warning: Unless you're the Narrator, *stop reading now!* This chapter contains notes to help run this adventure for you. You'll ruin the fun if you read ahead!

Note: If this is your first game of *Little Wizards*, you might want to start with "Bewitched Chocolate!" instead (*see page 70*).

Summary

In this Tale, our lil' Wizards visit the Steppes town of Baator, on the snowy slopes of the Malayak Mountains. There they encounter the Ermine tribe, whose guardian yak soon goes missing. During the search, the lil' Wizards run into a strange character, Gideon Herasmus, who has lost something of his own: a set of magic coins that let him travel anywhere on Coinworld (on either side)!

A pack of snow monkeys has run off with the coins, and Gideon is too afraid of the creatures to get the coins back. The Wizards can help Gideon recover his lost items. To show his gratitude, the explorer gives them an intriguing present: the key to a door in a mysterious manor. But that's another Tale...

Chapter 1: On the Road to Steppes

This Tale happens on Steppes, a place that may be new to the lil' Wizards. Assuming one of your Tales hasn't previously happened here, you'll need a good reason for the visit. Here are a few suggestions...

+ For lil' Mages, it could be a homework assignment for a class at Magic School: write a short essay about the Steppes Archipelago and the nomadic lifestyle of its tribes. Of course there are books about this topic, but Mages value field experience and prefer to see things for themselves whenever possible.

+ Lil' Sorcerers may come for a more practical reason, like collecting a tuft of hair from an albino yak that's only found on Steppes.

+ Maybe the Wizards have heard about the sledding festival on Steppes. They come for the fun and soon find themselves helping the Ermine tribe look for their missing yak.

- Let the players decide why their characters come to Steppes. It's their Tale, after all!

If you've just played "Bewitched Chocolate!" (*see page 70*), the lil' Wizards may be arriving from Smiles. In this case there are several options: they might catch a boat from Ellys, or perhaps they cross on broomstick from Curve's End.

Whatever their means of transport, the lil' Wizards arrive on Steppes at the main city of Baator on Malayak Island. The usual chaos of daily life is in full swing here, and the characters find themselves caught up in the hustle-bustle of it all…

....

Read to the Players

You arrive in Baator, Malayak's largest city. The harbor is loud with ship horns and the voices of shopkeepers calling out to passers-by in the streets.

The air is crisp and cold, but no one seems to care. Everyone's tightly wrapped in clothes made of thick yak wool.

....

Unless one of the Wizards is a native of Steppes, they probably don't speak the language and won't be able to read the street signs. They may get lost. If so, let them fumble a bit before introducing Berenicia (*see page 87*).

The specific vendors the Wizards encounter in the market are up to you, and this part of the Tale can be as short or long as you like. It's a good idea to go back and read (or re-read) the Steppes chapter (*see page 83*), as it contains lots of information you can use here. For example, woolen goods are prevalent. It's a harbor town, so fish and seafood are common as well.

Some shopkeepers are friendly and others are grumpy, but all are happy to trade with newcomers or accept their money (if the lil' Wizards have any). Again, there might be a language barrier (*see page 92*), and if anyone shops without knowing Steppish they'll have to wing it with grunts and gestures (which can be tons of fun to describe). If you like, ask for Brain rolls to communicate and/or Heart rolls to barter a good deal.

The primary goal of this chapter is to alert the Wizards that they could use a guide in this unfamiliar place, and that they have much to learn about it. Don't let the players get too frustrated, though! As soon as the street scene gets dull (and maybe before), introduce Berenicia as a friendly bystander who notices the Wizards need a little help. She steps in and translates for them, or aids their current purchase, and then walks them outside, making pleasant conversation along the way.

Berenicia invites the Wizards to a small coffee house (which also sells hot chocolate and pastries), and offers to teach them a spell that will let them speak and understand Steppish. She also happily answers any of the Wizards' questions about the archipelago and its culture, and suggests they accompany her to meet one of the tribes that's camped not far outside the city. She says this will be a wonderful learning opportunity for the Wizards, and it will be great fun as well!

Chapter 2: The Ermine Tribe

Outside the city, the lil' Wizards find a magnificent white landscape. The imposing shape of the Malayak Mountains looms on the horizon. It's not snowing, so flight conditions are good. That's lucky, because the Ermine camp is located at the foot of the mountain chain — a long walk but a short, quiet flight.

There's no need for Broom Riding rolls, but the air's icy cold and everyone should make a Very Easy (5) Body roll to avoid getting ill. Anyone who fails wind up sneezing, with a runny nose for the rest of the Tale.

From the foot of the mountain it's a short hike on crunchy white snow before the lil' Wizards arrive at the Ermine camp, which is nestled behind a tall hill...

Read to the Players

The sun sets on Malayak. A dozen yurts are huddled together, where the nomads are settling in for the night. Between the large tents, a herd of yaks peacefully grazes on a stack of hay bales. One of them has stark white fur.

One of the nomads calls out in greeting...

The tribe members warmly welcome Berenicia (she's well known and respected by the Ermine tribe), and in her company the lil' Wizards become honored guests.

The natives lead Berenicia and the Wizards to the chief's yurt as a crowd of the tribe's children look on with excited curiosity.

Mirnira, an old friend of Berenicia, welcomes the Wizards. The two ladies immediately dive into a passionate discussion that's incomprehensible to anyone else, and this is a great chance for the Wizards to explore the chief's yurt. They find cozy yak hair rugs, soft pillows, painted wall hangings, and many other attractive comforts.

After a few good laughs, the ladies turn their attention back to the guests. Mirnira greets the Wizards one by one, hugging them warmly. The rest of the tribe gathers in front of the yurt for an "official" reception, and Mirnira announces a welcoming party for tonight. Everyone wishes the Wizards a happy stay and the children ask endless questions about where they come from, why they look like they do, and of course, all about the rest of Coinworld (the children have lived their entire lives on Steppes, and marvel at everything else). Most of all they want to know about magic!

The Rules of Yak Horn

The first player to throw three rings onto his yak's horns wins the game. A roll of "1" is needed for the left horn and a "6" is needed for the right one.

When a character's turn comes up, he or she rolls...

+ *1d6 if the player's Heart Trait is Good (+0)*

+ *2d6 if the player's Heart Trait is Better (+1)*

+ *3d6 if the player's Heart Trait is Best (+2)*

+ *+1d6 if the player roleplays talking with his or her partner yak*

Turns continue until a player hangs 3 rings.

Eventually Mirnira saves the Wizards from this storm of questions and takes them to meet the yaks. She introduces the herd, and the characters meet the tribe's guardian yak: Ermine (the tribe was named after her). She's a magnificent albino creature with an intelligent gaze, and she instantly bonds with the Wizards. Her tail whips about excitedly at their presence, and she grunts happily if they pet her well-kept coat.

Berenicia departs, saying she is needed elsewhere. She leaves the lil' Wizards in the tribe's loving care and rides away on Coal, her familiar, who was staying with the tribe's herd. Mirnira tells the Wizards they can stay with the tribe as long as they want, and urges them to enjoy tonight's party. "It's in your honor, after all!"

The tribe gathers around a massive bonfire to enjoy the evening meal. It's a relaxing daily ritual for them but today they have special guests so everyone's smiles are a little bigger than usual. Steppish melodies are sung over dessert, and any Wizards with a cold are offered a big serving of Yakyurt, a local remedy (*see page 87*).

After supper the lil' Wizards are invited to a game of "Yak Horn" (*see left*). It's a very popular agility game in which a player is paired up with a yak and tries to throw as many iron rings around the beast's horns as possible. Communication between the thrower and the animal is critical, since the yak can help by moving his horns into the ring's path.

Once the party winds down, everyone retires to their yurts for a good rest. The lil' Wizards aren't forgotten — a small yurt is left for them, with all the amenities. They'll be quite cozy tonight.

Chapter 3: A Noise in the Night

At the foot of the Malayak Mountains, the night is silent and still. Even the wind has stopped blowing. Within the yurts everyone's sleeping tight, nomad and lil' Wizard alike — that is, until a strange noise wakes them all up.

The night air is cold — cold enough that no one wants to venture outside — but the sound was curious. Was it a yak coughing, or snow crunching, or something else... What's going on out there?

Lil' Wizards who don coats and head outside to investigate (or wind up outside shivering without their cold weather gear) find themselves under a clear sky full of beautiful twinkling stars. The peaks of the Malayak Mountains almost shimmer in the moonlight. It's a beautiful sight, and yet eerily quiet. The only disturbance is something happening near the yak herd.

Anyone who approaches the herd immediately notices that one of them is missing: Ermine, the albino. The tribe's guardian yak is gone!

Observant characters are helpful here (see page 75). They notice hoof tracks in the snow, leading up the nearest slope, away from the camp. It's likely that the lil' Wizards will start following these tracks. When they do, ask what they're taking with them. It's important to know whether they have their broomsticks, familiars, and other belongings, as they won't have anything they leave behind for the rest of the Tale.

The trail is easy to follow, but the climb is difficult due to the steep slope and the slippery ground. Anyone who's on foot (not using their broom) needs to make an Average (7) Body roll, with failure meaning they have a hard time with the climb and wind up covered in snow by the time they reach the peak. *Brrr!*

Riding brooms is easier but makes it harder to follow the trail. Unless one or more Wizards on the ground are leading broom riders with a source of light, flying characters must make a Very Hard (9) Brain roll to avoid losing sight of the hoof prints — and valuable time in the process.

After about an hour following the trail (or more if any broom riders lost their way), the lil' Wizards arrive at a cave entrance in the side of the mountain. The hook marks lead inside...

Chapter 4: A Strange Traveler

There doesn't appear to be any other way into the cave, and lights shined inside only reveal that it continues deep out of sight. The rest of this chapter assumes the lil' Wizards explore further.

. . . .

Read to the Players

A sound of dripping water echoes through the darkness and a howling wind rushes through the cave. Hang on to your hats!

After several steps over rocky ground and a few icy patches, you enter a gigantic natural grotto. Moonlight streams in through a small crevasse in the cave's roof.

Suddenly a man cries for help! He's somewhere deeper in the cave.

. . . .

Further on, the cavern widens and the Wizards discover a strange man hanging above a huge crack in the ice floor. Ermine holds a strap from the man's backpack in her teeth, and he somehow dangles awkwardly from the other strap. His legs flail above the chasm...

Read to the Players

The man struggles to keep hold of the one strap keeping him from falling into the chasm, and at the sight of you he gets very excited and calls out.

"Greetings, young ones! Or should I say good night?

"You find me in a very precarious situation! I slipped and nearly fell through the ice but fortunately this nice yak came to my rescue. Perhaps you'd be so kind as to offer a little help? I'd be most grateful..."

This is Gideon Herasmus, Coinworld explorer, and it's important that the lil' Wizards rescue him — but they don't have to know that! From the moment they see him it should be clear that Gideon is moments away from falling through the ice. Little by little the strap holding him up is tearing, and the Wizards can see that Ermine's hooves are slowly sliding across the wet ground, toward the chasm... The yak is trying her hardest, but Gideon is heavy and it's clear that unless the Wizards do something, and fast, both the explorer and Ermine will slide right out of sight.

This is a moment for the lil' Wizards to be creative.

Note to the Narrator: Time to Cheat!

Regardless of their methods, how much they fail, or even the number of Disasters they roll, the lil' Wizards eventually rescue Gideon. They have to for the Tale to continue! Fortunately, you can always cheat if you have to. That's one of your options as the Narrator, as we talked about in your chapter (see page 67).

So what can you do here? Well, you don't have to tell the players what their Difficulties actually are. This has two effects. First, it raises tension and focuses the players' attention less on the dice than on you (because they don't immediately know by seeing their Result whether they're successful, and so it all comes down to your description). Second, it lets you decide when one of their Actions succeeds, rescuing the explorer and the yak. You get to string the players along until they're squirming with suspense, and then let them win!

There are lots of ways they could rescue Gideon and Ermine and whatever they come up with — assuming it makes sense — should stand a chance to save the day. Let the players come up with something fun and inventive. Assign the Traits or Powers they use and the Difficulty they roll against; if they succeed, be sure to describe their last-second success with as much suspense as you can.

Even if the Action fails, it's not the end for Gideon and Ermine. Describe the yak slipping ever so much closer to the chasm and let the Wizards try something else. The important thing here is that the Wizards rise to the challenge and use some imagination — and if it comes down to it, don't forget to cheat (see page 67)!

Meanwhile...

Down at the camp, the first nomads wake up. They soon realize that both Ermine and the lil' Wizards are gone, and the whole tribe gathers to organize a search...

Chapter 5: Monkey Business

Once saved and safely away from the pit, Gideon thanks the lil' Wizards, introduces himself, and tells his story...

Read to the Players

"Many thanks, young wizards! I am Gideon Herasmus, explorer extraordinaire, and I am in your debt.

"You may be wondering how I came to be here. Well, I've spent my entire life traveling every corner of Coinworld, and I recently decided to climb the Malayak Mountains! I was camped up top there, and a pack of snow monkeys came to see what I was doing. Now, I don't think they meant any harm but they gave me quite the scare. I slipped and fell and... well, if it hadn't been for this here yak, and all of you of course, I might not be here to tell the story!

"I think the monkeys were scared too because they ran off up the mountain — which is a shame because they took something I need. It's the way I got here, you see... a magic set of coins that can take me anywhere on Coinworld!

"Could you help me out just one more time?"

The snow monkeys aren't far up the mountain. As Gideon says, they're harmless, but they're also a little nervous that they might have hurt the traveler. They have his satchel — full of the coins he mentioned — and they're arguing about what to do next. (Snow monkeys are notorious for bickering with each other. They can loudly debate a question until the answer doesn't matter anymore.)

Finding the monkeys is easy — they can be heard over the howling wind — but convincing them that no one's trying to steal the satchel is a bit tricky. Gideon is too winded to climb any higher, so the monkeys have no way to know the Wizards mean to help.

The good news is that the snow monkeys *want* to get the satchel back to Gideon, so all the Wizards need to do is convince the monkeys they want to the same thing. Here are a few ideas that could work...

+ The lil' Wizards could win the snow monkeys over by giving them some food, whether it's something they brought from the camp or something they whip up with Spellcasting or Alchemy. (The monkeys especially love frozen bananas and Yakyurt.)

- They could cast a spell, use a charm, or drink a potion to speak Snow Monkey (assuming Berenicia's solution from earlier doesn't already let them do so). Then all they have to do is explain themselves and succeed with an Average (7) Heart roll to convince the monkeys they intend to return the satchel.

- They could act like monkeys, leaping around and making monkey noises to bond with them. This could be a Body or Heart roll, with a Difficulty of Average (7), and Teamwork is allowed.

There are many other ways to convince the monkeys to return the satchel, and here again you should let the players guide the story. Any reasonable solution can become an Action, and any inventive plan could just succeed — though you'll want to maintain the suspense until the last moment, just so it doesn't seem too easy.

Even if the Wizards don't collect the satchel, the monkeys follow them back to Gideon to make sure it's delivered safely. They're overjoyed to see the explorer safe and unharmed, and play a little "monkey see, monkey do" with him and the Wizards before waving goodbye and heading back up the mountain.

Soon the nomads arrive. Mirnira lectures Ermine about running away but she can't stay angry with the yak for long and ends up giving Ermine a long, warm hug.

Gideon is all smiles as he looks through the satchel, making sure all the contents are still there. Sensing the lil' Wizards' curiosity, he's happy to explain...

Read to the Players

"Thank you so much for returning these to me!"

Gideon empties the satchel into the palm of his hand — five gold and copper coins with the shapes of island chains pressed into them. You recognize about half of the images — they're the archipelagos of Heads! But what are the others?

"These beauties.... These are very special. They're how I get around! You see, each face has an archipelago on it — ten faces for ten archipelagos! That's five here on Heads and five on Tails, the other side of Coinworld. Of course, I can't always control where I go... Each coin can take me to one of two places, and I have to flip for it. Pretty cool, eh?

"Oh, I have something for you!"

Gideon rummages through his backpack and pulls out a shining silver key. He holds it out for you to take.

"This is how you can get around! Just use this key to open any door and you'll go somewhere really fun!"

Then Gideon closes his eyes and picks one of his magic coins at random. He tosses it in the air and catches it, slapping it down on the back of his hand.

"Oh my, Whispers it is! Wonderful!"

He disappears with a "woof!" and the nomads all cheer his showmanship.

It's a short trip back to camp or to Baator. What's next? Maybe the Wizards use their new gift right away, in which case they find themselves in a spooky mansion on Shivers (*see page 109*). Or perhaps they stay on Steppes a while, learning more about the nomads and their wondrous homeland. Whatever they decide, the next Tale is right around the corner!

Epilogue

All's well that ends well. This visit to Steppes was eventful and rewarding. As Gideon resumes his travels on Whispers, the lil' Wizards are left with a key to... someplace else. It's a mystery, in more ways than one!

Remember to award Lil' Points for completing the Tale (plus any the players earned during the Tale, if you haven't given those out already).

The Shivers Archipelago

"Ah, the wonderful shiver that creeps up your spine when you first step on BentBack!" — Gideon Herasmus, tireless traveler

Flip Coinworld to Tails, where you find — among other things — the Shivers Archipelago. On this island chain, night lasts as long as it wants, and wind worms its way under your clothes and tickles your spine. Shivers may seem inhospitable to those unfamiliar with it, but those who live here like nothing better than a long, dark, and stormy night.

Four islands make up Shivers: **BentBack**, the **Island of Souls**, and the **Two Sisters**. The people who live on this archipelago are called Shiverers, their official language is called Shiverion, and their main currency is the Shivar (each of which is worth 10 Shivarets).

BentBack

Shivers' main island is home to several sleepy towns, most of which are nestled along gentle slopes and in shallow valleys. A well-established railway crosses the whole of the island from east to west, carrying steam locomotives to many stations along the way. The rail's main line links the two largest cities on BentBack.

The first city, **Bristly**, is built around a huge castle that's very properly haunted by several old ghosts. Bristly spreads out from the castle's feet. Along its narrow and windy cobblestone streets are many craftsmen, from carpenters to glass blowers to toy makers.

The second city, **Spikehair**, is located at the center of the island. It's a very busy place, with many oddly shaped gray stone buildings. The most famous of these structures is its library, as its bizarre architecture makes it look like an improbable layer cake. The manager, Mr. Roy, proudly proclaims to all the visitors that the museum's book collection includes a copy of every scary story ever written on Coinworld — every monster story, ghost story, and spooky fairy story ever put to paper.

The **Spooky Forest** covers most of the eastern half of BentBack. Its **clicking pines** cover much of the island's coldest terrain and hide many of the archipelago's greatest legends. To be honest though, the Spooky Forest isn't really all that scary — it's unsettling maybe, due to the howling wind, creaking branches, and baying wolves at night — but the truth of the matter is that the forest's reputation is cleverly promoted by BentBack's tourist bureau. The more people who believe BentBack is the scariest island on Coinworld, the more the locals can sell tour tickets and gift shop merchandise.

One of the Spooky Forest's most popular attractions is the **Breathless Pirate Lake**, where the cool, calm water reflects a moon that's nearly always out in full. The lake gets its name from the many pirate ghosts who stalk its shores. These ghosts often sail here from Bones after their deaths, though a few come from other parts of Tails as well. They wobble around on their peg legs with their ghost parrots on their shoulders, and host elaborate pirate shindigs until the wee hours of the morning. The bad spirit rum never stops flowing as these wannabe toughies share memories from their mortal lives, and occasionally shed a ghostly tear over what they left behind.

The Island of Souls

A strange atmosphere looms over the uninhabited forest at the center of the Island of Souls. In the dead of night, under the pale light of the moon, little balls of dazzling energy dance among the frozen pine trees. They perch on branches, wait and watch for a while, and then flit off to other high vantage points.

According to Shivers legend, these are lingering souls of the departed residents who are most attached to the island, gathering to celebrate from beyond the grave. The legend makes many tourists shudder, but the natives often call the show "enchanting."

There's a whole society of "soul seekers" who travel to the island to see the display, then return to share their experiences with others. These devoted women and men take their observations very seriously, and refuse to bring along anyone who doesn't share the same respect for the island's late residents.

The Two Sisters

These two smaller islands are located south of the Island of Souls. They owe their name to a sad old story that's forever etched in the memory of most Tails sailors. Ana and Lena were twin sisters, rare visitors from the Smiles Archipelago on Heads. On their way to BentBack to visit the great library in Bristly, their ship was caught in a storm and sank. The crew survived, but the twins were never found. These islands were renamed in their memory, and sailors navigating the straits between them observe a moment of silence every time they pass within sight of their shores.

Tale Seed: The Sisters' Secret

Somewhere at the bottom of the Two Sisters Straits — the thin strip of water between the islands — lies the wreckage of the twins' boat. This wreckage holds many silent secrets, some about the sisters' past and some about what they were *really* doing near Shivers' southern shores...

Living on Shivers

Life on Shivers is subject to the whims of night. It's often dark, sometimes *very* dark, as if the sun's rays are sulking and hiding away from the archipelago. Night can last for weeks at a time, especially during winter, which is very strange to those from other parts of Coinworld.

The archipelago's two main resources are wood and iron. Crafting and trade are common, and carpenters never run out of work building furniture made of clicking pine, whose doors creak and moan in a way that the Shiverers find pleasing. In a similar vein, nearly all of Coinworld's iron is forged on Shivers. Of course, many of the archipelago's numerous iron mines are haunted, but this only means that outsiders don't often mine them; Shiverers are happy to keep company with the ghosts, and in exchange the ghosts sometimes lead them to the best deposits.

Everyone on Shivers lives in a county (BentBack has six, and the Island of Souls and the Two Sisters have one each, for a total of nine). Each county is supervised by a small board of community officials, and these boards frequently include Mages (for better or for worse, Mages love to be involved in politics).

On BentBack and the Two Sisters, children start school at a very young age. There are many schools, and children are delivered to them via the archipelago's remarkable transportation system — which, you have to admit, is quite motivating (who wouldn't want to go to school on a large sled pulled by a pack of werewolves?). Shivers magic schools are part of a separate organization, and young Mages often switch once their talents emerge.

The most popular festival on Shivers is without doubt the Night O' Socks. Once a year, mysterious big-bellied characters dressed all in red enter homes through their chimneys and leave presents inside large socks hung just for the occasion. It's rumored that the distribution of presents is secretly orchestrated by the Schools of Magic, but no one has dared check the truth of this for fear of disrupting the celebration.

The Shivers Archipelago is well named, as its most common hobby is shared by everyone: scary stories by the fireplace. Young or old, girl or boy, everyone here loves the feeling of their breath catching in their throats, of the willies crawling up their backs, as a storyteller weaves a frightening tale. The art of storytelling is so important on Shivers that it's a subject taught in school. People gather in community centers, with friends, or with family to listen to a good scary story, and many of them pay for the privilege of hearing the scariest stories from professionals in huge theaters across the islands. A few of these pros are even Mages, adding sounds and light effects to their performances.

Haunted Locations and Night Creatures

The Shiverers' love of scary stories is explained by where they live. The archipelago has many haunted locations: aging manors, deep mines, dark groves, restless bays, and all sorts of other places where ghosts and night creatures are found.

Old dusty buildings are a favorite haunt, but ghosts are found everywhere. No one's alarmed to spot one shopping in the middle of town at noon on a Tuesday. They make great sports referees because they can watch from right in the middle of the action without getting in the

A Few Shiverion Phrases:

- *Hi!:* "Zdorovo"
- *Goodbye:* "Tynis yoko"
- *Thank you:* "Bolzin"
- *What a scare!:* "Ondoboy Jadim!"

way of the players (you can pass through them, after all). Ghosts become chefs, tailors, train conductors, police officers, and just about everything else.

There are also scary ghosts, and Shiverers know the difference. The locals are plenty scared when they run into a creepy spirit in the shadows of a basement, or as one emerges from a thick fog rolling in off the coast. It's a good thing Shiverers look forward to a good scare. They believe it keeps them in good health. Maybe it does. It's one of the reasons the spooky ghosts take their role in society so very seriously.

Shivers is home to other spooky creatures too, like werewolves and vampires. A werewolf is a human who can shift into a wolf at night, when the moon bathes the archipelago in its glow (and that's quite often, if you'll recall). Many werewolves join packs of real wolves so they don't have to howl at the moon alone. All werewolves have a wonderful ear for sounds, and a few have become recognized composers, or joined one of the lupine choirs that record and sell music all across Tails. Other werewolves still find a way to make themselves useful, whether it's pulling sleds of kids to school or showing people to their seats in one of the many theaters on the archipelago (werewolves also see very well in the dark, so they don't have to disturb the performers when someone shows up late).

Vampires are pretty traditional folk, and a bit vain. Most of them wear black satin cloaks, keep their jutting fangs nicely polished, and view everyone with a bewitching gaze. They only leave home at night, not because the sun hurts them but because they think the softer light of the moon looks better on their pale features. They sleep in custom-made coffins during the day because they're insecure about sleeping where anyone can see them (after all, you can't control what you look like when you're snoozing). Their coffins are well insulated — vampires also like it cool — and both the coffins and the crypts where they're usually kept are designed and built by Shivers' excellent craftspeople. Vampires are excellent customers; they value quality and regularly order new coffins to stay fashionable.

Wizards and the Shivers

In a place where a ghost, a vampire, and a werewolf can be seen on any given day (or, rather, night), no one looks twice at a Wizard riding a broomstick or stirring a cauldron.

Shivers has several Schools of Magic that all fall under the authority of the BentBack High College in Bristly. This 60-foot-high carved stone tower *looks* to be crumbling under its own weight, about to collapse at any moment. The Mages keep it together, though, and maintain the impossible curve that makes it such a unique architectural curiosity.

The High College is led by High Mage Balderdash Dormidor, who's easily recognizable thanks to his splendid gray mustache. Balderdash is a gruff man who likes to scare the youngest Mages with creepy stories about the College and its turbulent past. He's also very good at his job, knowing exactly how to get the best out of everyone around him.

Beyond classic magic tradition, Shivers Mages also study the domains of Darkness and Light, and the mysteries of "What Lies Beyond." The High Mage Council oversees this research, as it must be carefully controlled. "The dead should under no circumstances be disturbed," the Council says. "They deserve just as much respect as the living. Perhaps more."

Weird Object: Shivering Flute

Shivering flutes are carved from clicking pine, a special wood found only on this archipelago. These instruments are very hard to master. In the hands of a trained player, their soft low-pitched melodies can trigger delicious chills of fear. In untrained hands, their sound can make you cringe.

Sorcerers come in many forms on Shivers, but they all have one thing in common: they live according to their own rules! Refusing to adopt the rigid conventions of the Mage Schools, Shivers Sorcerers find their own way, and each is as special as what they do for a living. Some become "mediums" who speak with ghosts, though on Shivers this has less to do with the ability to converse with them (everyone can do that!), and more to do with sensing what ghosts want and making them happy (they're like counselors — for the dead).

Other Sorcerers withdraw from the towns, living in the wilderness and studying the magic of nature. They brew incredible potions and salves with ingredients they collect in Shivers' deep forests, and use them to protect the denizens of the roughs. Occasionally they'll part with one of their unique concoctions, for a favor to be collected later...

Then there are the Sorcerers who specialize in Spellcasting. On Shivers many of them are stage performers, frightening crowds with their flashy charms, unpredictable personalities, and keen senses of dark humor. A few performers hit the streets, unable or unwilling to take jobs at the big stage houses, but content to deliver a good shock to those waiting for the next train. Other Sorcerer Diviners excel as curio shop owners (it's hard to pull one over on someone who can actually tell if an object is magical).

Someone to Meet

Here's a character the lil' Wizards might meet on the Shivers Archipelago...

Balderdash Dormidor, Dean of the BentBack High College

Balderdash is a proper Mage elder, imperious and wise. His face is hidden behind an enormous gray mustache, and he walks with a tall cane topped with a knot of wood larger than his head. He has led the BentBack College for so long that people say he was installed with the furniture. He wanders the halls and stairs, grumbling at everyone he meets, but he means well. Balderdash isn't a bad guy — he's just trying to ensure that everything in the college goes as smoothly as possible, and that all the pupils learn everything they can.

HIS TRAITS
Body: Better (+1)
Heart: Better (+1)
Brain: Best (+2)

HIS SKILLS
Leadership
Tattle-Tales

HIS POWERS
Broom Riding: Best (+2)
Spellcasting: Best (+2)
Conjuring: Best (+2)

HIS BELONGINGS
A walking stick carved from clicking pine
A notebook with each student's class schedule
Magic eyeglasses with unknown powers (because really, how could they be *just* eyeglasses?)

HIS FAMILIAR
Nebula, a sarcastic laughing bat that's particularly sensitive to the cold

Animals and Plants

Laughing Bat

Depending on their size and gender, these small mammals can emit all kind of laughs, from adorable to irritating, sarcastic to bellowing. They like heat and darkness, which is easily found in Shivers' attics.

Lemmings

Lemmings are small, furry rodents that live and travel in packs (sometimes as large as a hundred at a time). They're also greedy and stubborn; they'll intently follow someone for miles for a tiny sliver of their favorite food.

Clicking Pine Tree

The clicking pine tree is a tall conifer found everywhere on Shivers but especially in the east. It's named for the odd noise its needles make when they're blown by the wind, which is reminiscent of colliding skeleton bones.

Shivermoss

Shivermoss is a thin gray plant that coats rocks along the archipelago's rivers and sea shores. It's also found on the slopes of active volcanoes, like the ones in the north of BentBack. Shivermoss gets its name from an uncontrollable reaction to human touch: it twitches when gently caressed, as if purring.

Moon Herb

Moon herb is a tall and elegant grass generally found on hillsides. It can only be seen and picked when the moon is full; it's invisible at all other times. Moon herb is a component for several alchemical formulas, and Sorcerers travel from all over Coinworld to restock.

A Tale: The Squeakydoor Manor Mystery

Warning: As with all Tales, if you aren't the Narrator you should stop reading now!

Note: "The Squeakydoor Manor Mystery" assumes you've already played "Lost in Malayak" *(see page 90)*. Also, if this is your first game of *Little Wizards*, you might want to play "Bewitched Chocolate!" before anything else *(see page 70)*.

Summary

At the end of "Lost in Malayak," the lil' Wizards received a strange key and were told to use it in any door — *any door!* — to go somewhere really fun. The truth is that no matter what door is chosen, it opens into the Squeakydoor Manor on the Shivers Archipelago. Yes, it opens to the *other side of Coinworld!*

The Squeakydoor Manor is a hotel on BentBack island. Just now, the manor hosts a strange group of guests, each with part of a magic medallion. When assembled, the medallion unlocks a chest in the manor's basement.

To solve the Squeakydoor Manor mystery, the lil' Wizards have to convince each of the guests to part with their medallion fragment. Along the way, they may also have the chance to bring the other guests together so they can all realize some of their fondest dreams.

Running the Tale

This Tale differs from "Bewitched Chocolate!" and "Lost in Malayak" in that the players have a lot of choice in how to proceed. This means the Narrator won't always have quite as much information specific to what the lil' Wizards will probably do, and so she'll need to adapt to their choices and Actions, and improvise whenever a necessary detail isn't included here.

The first and most important step is to read, reread (and maybe even re-reread) the Tale to gain a firm understanding of the location and characters. Don't hesitate to take notes, or if it helps, to make drawings. You really can't prepare enough for a Tale like this!

The second step is to decide whether to include the various subplots for the other guests — specifically the chance to bring them together to put on a stage show at the hotel, or convert the hotel into a theater to put on plays and musicals. This part of the Tale isn't necessary to solve the mystery but it makes the other guests feel a little more real and offers more detail for your descriptions. It also gives the Wizards the chance to do something really sweet and helpful during their visit.

The final step is to photocopy the game aids (see pages 112 and 123). The first one is a map of the manor, which everyone will use to describe where their characters go. The second is a picture of the medallion, which you can print on cardstock and cut into six pieces (each of the two center circles is a separate piece), so you can actually hand the players the pieces as they find them in the story.

The Manor's Secret

The Squeakydoor Manor is owned by a nervous fellow named Mr. Filmon. He inherited the manor from his uncle and found it such an exciting place, in such a touristy part of the world, that he figured he'd convert it into a hotel.

Unfortunately, Mr. Filmon soon discovered the hotel already had a guest — a ghost! Even if the ghost did live there first, Mr. Filmon believed the spirit would be bad for business, and so he tried to chase it away. When the ghost refused to leave, Mr. Filmon purchased a magic chest and lured the ghost inside. He slammed the lid shut and removed the medallion that acts as the chest's key, breaking it into six pieces.

With the ghost gone, business flourished. Season after season the guests kept coming. Then one day Mr. Filmon accidentally left the medallion pieces out as the previous night's guests were finishing breakfast. Assuming the fragments were souvenirs of their stay, each guest took one — but one guest was curious...

Gideon Herasmus was among the guests at breakfast that morning. He was curious about the strange gift but also running late for a new adventure, so he left his fragment behind with a note to the future occupant of his room. He made sure the room was paid up and kept an eye out for someone to solve the mystery for him.

When Gideon met the Wizards on Steppes (in "Lost in Malayak"), he recognized in them the ingenuity needed to solve the mystery. He gave them the key to his room at the manor — after having it magically charmed to open any door anywhere on Coinworld and reveal his Squeakydoor room beyond — and trusted that they would satisfy his curiosity.

The Manor

The Squeakydoor Manor sits in the cold north of BentBack Island. It's an old building, made of cut stone. Its ivy-covered exterior walls look decrepit but it's all a show for the tourists — they're actually quite sturdy.

The manor has two floors built around an inner courtyard. Inside the atmosphere is posh, with waxed wooden floors and thick wall hangings. Oil lamps hang from silver fixtures, providing soft light in every room.

THE GROUND FLOOR

The manor's huge **front double doors** lead directly into a wide **hallway** lined with portraits of all the previous owners. This hallway circles all the way around the building with doors into every room on the floor, plus the inner courtyard. A few windows in the hallway also open into the courtyard, and at the back of the manor two squeaky wooden staircases lead upstairs.

The manor's **reception desk** is in the hall directly across from the double doors. Nearby are hooks with keys to all of the manor's rooms, plus the guest book and a copper bell. There's also a reading corner with a few old issues of the *BentBack Chills*, a popular Shivers newspaper.

The door to the **storeroom** is locked to protect the manor's supplies from hungry insomniacs. Its shelves are filled with yummy snacks and drinks.

Mr. Filmon's room is kept locked except for the few hours a day that he sleeps. There are two things to find here, both in his writing desk: the only key to the wood shed (which Mr. Filmon uses every night before bed to check on the magic chest in the basement), and a receipt for the purchase of a "custom chest with a magical lock mechanism" from a furniture maker in Bristly.

The **kitchen** is where Mr. Filmon spends most of his time. He cooks all the meals for his guests, and while he's busy here it's best to stay out of his way. Anyone who enters when he's preparing meals for the guests is shooed away — at first politely, but then with loud irritation.

The **laundry** smells of clean sheets and detergent. Mr. Filmon keeps this room locked at all times. That's too bad — it's the perfect place to whip up a ghost costume to haunt the manor's corridors!

The **dining room** is the manor's largest location. The centerpiece is a massive oak table surrounded by comfortable chairs with tall padded backs. Beautiful silver candelabras are placed on the lace tablecloth, as well as the surrounding serving tables. A fireplace is built into the room's back wall.

The **living room** is a place where guests can relax, talk, and read, or just enjoy the warmth of the manor's second fireplace. Observant characters *(see page 75)* notice the ornate antique clock located here is no longer working.

Finally, the **library** is well stocked with classics of scary Shivers literature (as if there's any other kind!). There are also books about the manor's history, including a tragic story about its first owners, whose son — an adventurous and giving lad with a gift for performance — went missing in the surrounding forest, never to be seen again. A recent addition to the library is a whole shelf of books by someone simply named "The Bard," which includes a huge number of densely written but extremely lyrical poems and stage plays.

THE SECOND FLOOR

All but one of the rooms on this floor are rented **guest rooms.** Rooms 1, 2, 5, 6, and 7 are occupied (by guests introduced in the next section). Room 3 is rented out to Gideon Herasmus, and Room 4 is available for new guests.

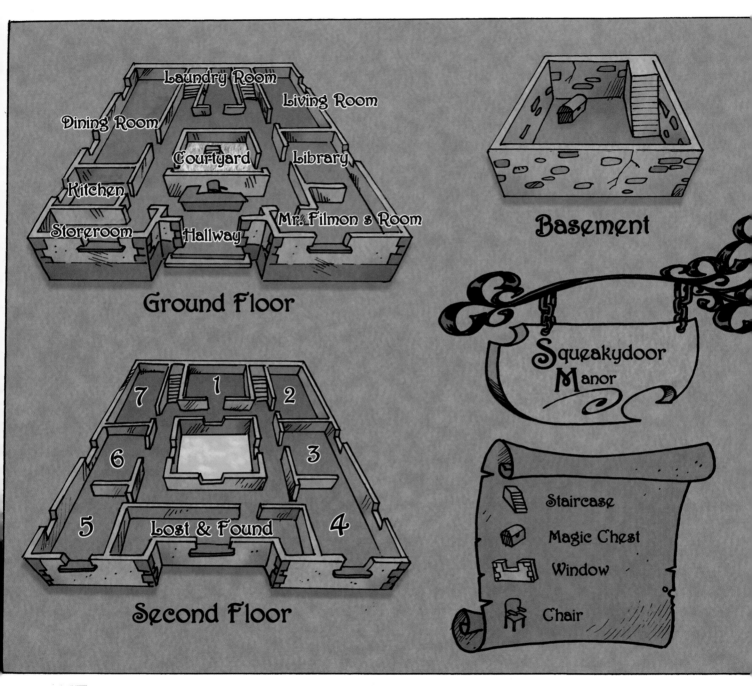

Ground Floor

Laundry Room
Living Room
Dining Room
Courtyard
Library
Kitchen
Storeroom
Hallway
Mr. Filmon's Room

Basement

Squeakydoor Manor

Second Floor

7 1 2
6 3
5 Lost & Found 4

Staircase

Magic Chest

Window

Chair

Permission granted to photocopy for personal use only.

The last room on the second floor is the **lost & found**. It contains the clothes, luggage, nick-knacks, and other miscellaneous objects left behind by former guests, all caked with a thick layer of dust. It's also a lonely home to several rodents and spiders. The one window in this room is papered over so no one can see the junk stored here. (Observant characters may spot the paper on the windows from outside the building.)

THE INNER COURTYARD

A thin layer of frost covers the lawn and plants here until midday, at which point Mr. Filmon picks whatever's ripe from the aromatic herbs in his **vegetable garden**. A washing line stretches across the courtyard, though it's only used in the late afternoon (which on Shivers means it sometimes can't be used for days or weeks at a time).

A wood shed stands in the center of the inner courtyard, its door firmly shut with a heavy rusted padlock. The shed has no windows and contains piles of wood for the manor's fireplaces. It also hides the entrance to the basement — under an ugly old rug and sealed with another padlock.

The Other Guests

Not counting the ghost locked in the basement chest, the Squeakydoor Manor currently hosts five colorful characters plus the owner, Mr. Filmon. All of them are detailed in the following pages, with information about their goals and motivations, what can be found in their rooms, and how to obtain their medallion fragments.

MR. FILMON

The owner of the Squeakydoor Manor is a short man in his fifties with old-fashioned glasses and a hooked nose. He's friendly but distracted, his mind focused on all the work to keep the hotel running. Cleaning, cooking, room service... He almost never sleeps!

Secretly, Mr. Filmon is a great lover of classic poems and stage plays. In fact, he was just about to open a theater in Spikehair before his uncle left him the manor. This is why all those books by The Bard are in the library — they're Mr. Filmon's all-time favorites, full of music and tragedy and spooky characters and ideas. He still thinks there's a market for a revival of those stories on the stage, and he hopes that one day he'll be able to make that happen. For now though, he has a hotel to run!

Every evening after dinner, Mr. Filmon visits the wood shed, ostensibly to restock the wood for each fireplace. Observant characters may notice that he's in the shed a long time, however, which is because it's when he checks on the magic chest. Only when he knows the ghost is still locked up can he settle in for a good (though short) night's sleep. He keeps the basement key in his writing desk drawer (in his room) at all times except during these late night trips.

Note to the Narrator:

Note to the Narrator: Ways and Means

Each guest has a specific suggestion for how the Wizards might acquire their medallion fragment. There are other options, though...

+ **Persuasion:** *A sympathetic story or a good argument can work wonders, especially for Wizards with a big Heart.*

+ **Deceit:** *A small animal — like maybe a lil' familiar — could sneak away with one of the fragments. The Wizards could pretend to be part of housekeeping to get into a room. There are lots of underhanded ways to gain the fragments, but stealing and lying should always have consequences for the culprits!*

+ **Fear:** *By pretending to be ghosts or another scary thing the Wizards could frighten a guest into giving up their fragment. This is Shivers, after all. These guests might like a good scare!*

+ **Swaps:** *Miss Hasbin wants a mirror. Count Gregory has a mirror he doesn't need, but he wants Mac Piston's sound dampener. Mac will part with the sound dampener for a little of Captain Graybeard's treasure, and so on. Can the lil' Wizards make all the necessary swaps to get all the medallion fragments?*

PUMPKIN JACK

A giant pumpkin rests on this little guy's shoulders, and it's as orange as it gets. His glowing red eyes and large, sharp-toothed smile are more than a little unnerving. He'll give you a good fright unless you see him coming! Why does Jack look this way? Even he doesn't know.

Pumpkin Jack is an aspiring oil painter and specializes in beautiful portraits and grand panoramic vistas. He came to the manor to find some new terrain for his latest series but since his arrival he's found that he's much more interested in painting a lasting tribute to a different beauty: Miss Hasbin.

- **His guest room:** Room 6, very classic and formal, with easels, paints, and incomplete masterpieces everywhere, including many of Miss Hasbin

- **How to get his medallion fragment:** Just ask him. Most people avoid Jack, so he's very happy to chat with anyone who'll listen, and even a few minutes of pleasant conversation are worthy of his fragment.

MISS MELODY HASBIN

Regardless of her plans for the day, Miss Hasbin is always dressed to the nines, with an elegant gown and gorgeous jewels, and her blonde hair twisted up into a fancy knot. She always looks like a beauty queen.

Melody recently retired from show business but she's still as creative as ever and her voice has lost none of its power. She practices in her room and while she keeps the door closed, her voice still echoes throughout the manor. People with sensitive ears may want to invest in earplugs!

- **Her guest room:** Room 5, which has a large canopy bed, pink decor, and a dressing table with no mirror

- **How to get her medallion fragment:** Bring her a mirror so she can practice her facial expressions as she sings

CAPTAIN MORTIMER R. GRAYBEARD

This old mariner is always talking about his youth on the seas of Coinworld. To hear him tell it, he's seen and done everything there is to see and do on the wide ocean waves, and nothing and no one will ever live a more adventurous life than his.

Mortimer has a peg leg, an eye patch, and a grumpy demeanor. He's constantly smoking a foul-smelling pipe, says everything loudly, and knows an impressive number of funny near-curses ("By the Kraken's nostrils!" and "Hairy peg leg!" are two of his favorites). Mortimer always wears his pirate hat, even when sleeping.

- **His guest room:** Room 2, which he's done up to look like a ship cabin, with a hammock, maritime maps, and a real cannon pointed out the window! He even has a "treasure horde" — really just a big pile of very pretty rocks he's collected from all over Coinworld — which he keeps locked in a small chest under his bed.

- **How to get his medallion fragment:** Pay for it with some loot, by golly! A big purse full of coins would be fine, or maybe a trinket from Heads...

MAC PISTON

Mac Piston is a loopy old tinkerer. Hidden behind thick glasses and a bushy mustache, he grumbles all the time, complaining about careless people breaking things he has to fix. Repairing things is what makes Mac Piston tick — a whack with a hammer here, a turn of a screwdriver there, a bolt tightened, a rewound spring, and there we go, it works! His job is done... for now.

Another thing Mac Piston likes to do is take working things apart, and sometimes he forgets to put them back together. All too often he'll play around with something in the manor, get bored or distracted, and leave his new toy broken. Mr. Filmon knows that Mac has good intentions, and it's terribly useful to be able to call on the tinkerer when something stops working — whether it's because Mac played around with it or not — so the owner forgives the old coot's experiments.

+ **His guest room:** Room 1, which looks more like a workshop than anything else. Tools and spare parts are strewn all over the place, seemingly without rhyme or reason. Mac's even converted the bathroom into a testing room for his sound dampener, which looks like an old gramophone but sucks in sound instead of pushing it out. Mac uses the sound dampener to kill the noise of his loudest tinkering (hammering mostly, but sometimes when he rips stuff apart).

+ **How to get his medallion fragment:** Repair the only object he's never been able to fix — the living room clock. Jury-rigging it won't work but a bit of magic might...

COUNT GREGORY

The Count is a young vampire from Spikehair City. He looks very distinguished with his ruffled shirt, high collar, and long suede coat. He speaks with a lisp, probably because of his jutting fangs. The Count is here for some rest and relaxation, far from the city and its bustle. Unfortunately, he finds Miss Hasbin's constant singing to be quite irritating, and is thinking about moving somewhere else for the rest of his vacation.

The irony is that the Count thinks Miss Hasbin has a really beautiful voice; he just doesn't like opera very much. Back in Spikehair, the Count is a respected and successful music producer, known for managing several high-profile singing groups. His heart has always been in producing for the stage, though — he dreams of one day putting on the world's best live scary musical.

+ **His guest room:** Room 7, which is covered in red and black velvet and illuminated with rows and rows of flickering candles. The Count has had the bed removed and replaced with a coffin. All the windows are covered with heavy drapes.

- **How to get his medallion fragment:** The Count is sick of Miss Hasbin's loud practicing but he's too polite to ask her to stop. Maybe the lil' Wizards can find a way for him not to hear her anymore, rather than ruin her fun. (Mac Piston's sound dampener would do the trick, if the Wizards can convince him to let them borrow it, or if he could be talked into building another one for the Count.)

GIDEON HERASMUS

Gideon was in Room 3 and his bill is paid up for another two days. His room is tidy and clean, and one of the medallion fragments is located in the drawer of his writing desk (he didn't leave it out in case Mr. Filmon came in to clean). A note is tucked in with the fragment, which is presented in full in "The Wizards Arrive" (see page 118).

THE SQUEAKYDOOR MANOR GHOST

Poor ghost! He's friendly and courteous but he's always playing jokes, which can sometimes be startling. It's just like when he was alive, back when the manor was first built by his family. He ran out into the forest and hid, planning to jump out and scare his sister when she came looking for him. She never came and when he started back home he got lost in the woods. The next thing he knew he was a ghost, floating around and scaring everybody without even trying!

A family of ghosts found and adopted him, and they loved him like he was their own son. They encouraged his hobbies, even when they weren't very practical — like his dream of performing on stage. Many years later the ghost returned to the manor and moved into his old room (the same one rented by Gideon Herasmus). He haunted the place for a long time, until Mr. Filmon inherited it and turned it into a hotel.

At first the ghost was excited to see so many new people, but he couldn't help scaring everyone, and even though they seemed to like it, Mr. Filmon wasn't pleased. He didn't take the time to get to know the ghost, and instead locked him in a magic chest. Now the ghost is alone and bored, and wondering when he'll get to play again.

If the lil' Wizards manage to free the ghost and speak with Mr. Filmon on his behalf, perhaps the two of them can find a happy compromise and make the hotel an even bigger success — because after all, tourists come to Shivers to be *scared*, not to rest and relax!

The Wizards Arrive

The Tale starts when the lil' Wizards use the key Gideon Herasmus gave them at the end of "Lost in Malayak." Any lock in any door will do — the key magically fits no matter what door the Wizards try, and with a loud click it opens into Room 3 of the Squeakydoor Manor (Gideon's room, where he stayed before traveling to Steppes).

The charm cast on the key also causes it to softly hum when the lil' Wizards arrive, and the humming gets louder as they approach the writing desk where Gideon left his medallion fragment. The humming abruptly stops when the desk drawer is opened, revealing the fragment and a note that reads...

Read to the Players

Glad you could come! You've been transported to the Squeakydoor Manor on the Shivers Archipelago on Tails. This is my room and you're more than welcome to stay here. I have also left an intriguing item for you, which is one piece of six that make up a whole medallion. When I departed the manor, the other five pieces were in the possession of the other guests staying here.

I believe the medallion is part of a mystery in the manor — something involving the owner, Mr. Filmon. See if you can find out what's going on, will you? I would be most grateful for the help. It would put my curious mind at ease.

Sincerely,

Gideon Herasmus

P.S. As I mention, I believe Mr. Filmon is somehow at the center of the mystery. It would be best not to ask him about it, and to be careful what you tell anyone until you find out what's going on. Just to avoid any awkward moments, you understand.

The lil' Wizards have a few moments to take this in and look around the room before Mr. Filmon arrives, having heard the key's humming while he was cleaning a nearby guest room. He is at first surprised and irritated by the intrusion, but then he sees the key and realizes the kids must be the ones Gideon told him would be arriving to stay in the room. Here's what Mr. Filmon's first words to them might be...

"What are you doing in here? Hmmm... This is Mr. Herasmus' key. He mentioned that someone would be coming to stay in his room but I never guessed there would be so many of you! Fortunately we've just had a cancelation and the room next door is free as well. Some of you can stay there — unless I get another paying guest, in which case you'll all have to crowd in here. Here's the key. It's Room 4 in the corner.

"Meals are at 8, noon, and 6. You're free to enjoy all the open rooms on the first floor, and there's plenty of beautiful scenery outside. This room's paid up for the next two days, so please enjoy your stay!"

Mr. Filmon gives the lil' Wizards a few moments to stammer out any questions they might have, and then departs. He's very busy with cleaning the other rooms right now and has to get to the laundry and lunch preparations very soon.

Unless the lil' Wizards hide the medallion fragment when Mr. Filmon comes in, the key's charm has one final effect (unless you want it to have more, of course): it turns Gideon's fragment invisible while Mr. Filmon is present, so the hotel owner doesn't notice that the new guests have the fragment in hand. (Gideon is nothing if not a careful planner, and doesn't want his new helpers found out before they can learn what's going on.) Sadly, this effect only works once; from now on the Wizards have to be careful if they want to avoid anyone seeing any fragments they have.

After Mr. Filmon leaves, the lil' Wizards can investigate as they wish. When they exit the room through the door they used to arrive, they find themselves in the manor's second floor hallway, their previous location nowhere to be seen. How will they get home? They can figure that out later — right now there's a mystery to solve!

Lil' Investigators!

Initially the lil' Wizards don't know much about what's going on. Gideon's note mentions that Mr. Filmon is involved (and gives the impression that he may be doing something bad). There are five more pieces of the medallion to collect, but why the medallion is important and what to do with it once all the pieces are assembled are not known. Because of this, the players may not feel confident about what they're supposed to do.

Fortunately, not having a clear direction isn't a huge issue in this Tale. There's still plenty for the lil' Wizards to do and it should all come naturally, like meeting and speaking with the other manor guests. In fact, this is how the lil' Wizards can learn a few of the most important clues about the Squeakydoor mystery.

Here's an overview of what the other guests are doing when the lil' Wizards arrive, plus what they think about the medallion fragments and how they're using them. With these notes and the information in "The Other Guests" *(see page 113)*, you should be able to improvise encounters with them, and casually provide details to help the Wizards solve the mystery.

- **Pumpkin Jack** likes Miss Hasbin — as more than a friend — and he spends a lot of time studying her so he can paint a portrait to give her as a present. He also chats with Captain Graybeard about the pirate's high seas exploits, and since his curiosity has been piqued by the medallion fragments he also wants to know if the Captain has ever seen anything like them before (he hasn't, but he has his own theories about what they are).

- **Miss Hasbin** has decided her fragment will make a great broach, and she wants Mac to make the adjustments (he's focused on other things right now, and mostly ignores her). Otherwise she focuses on her singing and tries to work up the courage to talk to Count Gregory about a scary new musical she's written (she's hoping he will help produce the show).

- **Captain Graybeard** thinks the fragments are a treasure map, and tries to acquire the other pieces so he can go find a new fortune. Unfortunately, he's so loud and crusty that no one but Pumpkin Jack will listen to him. When not trying to talk the others out of their fragments, Mortimer is in the library researching the manor's history for mentions of the medallion (thus, he might know the story about the boy who went missing in the forest).

- **Mac Piston** frets about the broken clock in the living room, upset that he can't get it working again. The rest of the time he pesters Mr. Filmon about a bunch of upgrades he wants to make to the hotel, like turning the basement into a workshop (this might be the first time the lil' Wizards hear about the basement, and observant characters may notice that there's no apparent staircase leading down from the ground floor). Mac is using his fragment as a counterweight in a contraption in his room (it's the perfect size and weight, and he won't want to give it up without something to replace it).

- **Count Gregory** just wants to be left alone so he can enjoy some peace and quiet (back in Spikehair he's always on the go). He took this trip to find his groove again, and maybe work up the courage to break away from the singing groups he's been managing so he can put on a spooky stage show. He would love Miss Hasbin's musical if he heard it, but all she sings is her *arpeggios* (she's practicing hard, hoping her voice will be at its best when she works up the courage to perform for the Count). Gregory has tucked his medallion fragment into his luggage to give to his son when he gets back to Spikehair.

- **Mr. Filmon** is barely keeping up with the needs of the hotel, and wants to hire some help (one of the best ways to get on his good side is to pitch in with his duties). He's on the lookout for the medallion, which he thinks he's misplaced (he can't remember where he last put it down). Anytime the Tale gets slow, Mr. Filmon can find or notice another guest's fragment. Depending on who has it, they might simply give it back with an apology, or argue that it was a gift. This is a chance for the lil' Wizards to jump in and help negotiate, and it also brings the focus back to the mystery at the center of the Tale.

The lil' Wizards can snoop around instead of talking to the other guests. They might learn any of the details in the previous section in this fashion, and they could also spot Mr. Filmon as he sneaks off to the wood shed at night to check on his magic chest *(see page 122)*.

Let the players guide the investigation. There's a lot to find out, but they don't need to learn everything. Keep them focused on the main mystery if you can, and encourage them to come up with their own theories about what's happening, and ways to collect the other fragments. Make up whatever new details you like and if you feel confident enough you can even change things around. Remember that you can drop anything that doesn't work for you, and if you need to simplify the Tale it's easy to remove everything about the stage show. All that matters is that everyone has fun along the way!

Ring the Dinner Bell!

If the lil' Wizards are stuck, Mr. Filmon calls everyone down to dinner. He's prepared an elaborate meal in the dining room, which brings all the guests together in a casual, comfortable environment. This is an excellent chance for the Wizards to socialize a bit, and if they're shy the other guests can ask *them* questions — about their stay, their previous adventures, and anything else you think they might find interesting.

Sprinkle some clues and other details from the previous sections into the dinner talk, but be careful not to have any of the other guests reveal their fragments when Mr. Filmon is looking. If the Wizards reveal theirs,

Note to the Narrator: Speaking in Character

When speaking as the other guests, keep in mind what the players are hearing. If you think the players might be confused about when you're speaking as a character vs. when you're speaking directly to them as the Narrator, you can adopt a simple voice for each guest. For example, you might speak with slow and deep words as Pumpkin Jack, or with a pirate accent as Captain Graybeard.

You can also use motions to indicate when you're speaking as a character. You could steeple your fingers as Jack or hold one eye closed as Captain Graybeard (because he wears an eyepatch).

the hotel owner gets very excited and thanks them for returning his lost items. It's up to you whether the other guests give their pieces back at this point as well (it's most interesting if at least one or two don't, but it speeds things up if all the fragments are together).

Of course, the lil' Wizards can refuse to return their fragment(s) and Mr. Filmon won't demand they do. This is sure to cause an awkward moment for everyone, however, and afterward Mr. Filmon gets even more nervous around the Wizards. He may try to talk them into returning the fragments later, if you think it will make the Tale more interesting, or he might simply avoid the Wizards for the rest of their stay.

Dinnertime is also a great chance for the Wizards to look around in places that might otherwise be occupied, without fear that someone will walk in. They can skip a meal or slip away early to look in the other guest rooms, or even Mr. Filmon's room or the wood shed.

Throughout every meal Mr. Filmon remains his typical nervous self. Observant characters notice that he spends most of his time glancing toward the wood shed.

Mr. Filmon Visits the Wood Shed

After dinner, Mr. Filmon sneaks away to visit the inner courtyard and enters the wood shed, where he stays for much longer than is necessary to restock the manor's fireplaces. He is, of course, checking on the magic chest that holds the ghost.

If the Wizards enter the wood shed while Mr. Filmon is inside they find the rug pulled aside, revealing an open trapdoor and a staircase leading down. Heading down, they hear Mr. Filmon's voice before they reach the bottom step. He's reading aloud...

"Stay! Speak, speak! I charge thee, speak!"

Mr. Filmon is sitting alone on a stool, reading from a book in front of a large wooden chest with silver and steel banding. Observant characters notice the chest has a circular depression instead of a keyhole, and if the Wizards have at least two medallion fragments (giving them an idea of its rough size and shape) they figure the complete item will fit perfectly into this space.

The hotel owner is so engrossed in what he's reading that unless the lil' Wizards call attention to themselves he doesn't immediately notice them. His voice drops off for a moment and he places his hand on the chest, as if he's deeply sad about something. He finishes from memory...

"'Tis gone, and will not answer."

A draft blows through the room that brings a chill with it. The lil' Wizards shiver involuntarily, and observant characters may think they hear something on the wind, a whisper maybe. It's gone a second later and those who noticed it are left wondering if it was just their mind playing a trick on them.

Mr. Filmon looks up, noticing the Wizards for the first time. He slams the book shut and blurts out, "You're not supposed to be here! Go on! This place isn't for you!" He ushers the kids back up the stairs and out of the wood shed, locking both the trapdoor and the shed door behind them (they of course see the key he uses, which he pulls from his pocket). Mr. Filmon refuses to speak about the basement or the chest, and he demands the Wizards leave the courtyard. "Back inside! You'll catch your death of cold out here!"

If the lil' Wizards follow Mr. Filmon after he chases them back inside, he returns the book to the library, alongside a full shelf of books from the same series, all by someone named "The Bard." He then retires to his room, taking the wood shed key with him. The whole time he looks less nervous than sad. Something is weighing very heavily on him.

This is the magical medallion that opens the chest in the manor basement. You can make a copy of this page and cut the fragments apart, pasting each to a piece of cardboard (or download a separated version from **crafty-games.com**). This way you can hand the actual fragments to the players as the lil' Wizards find them.

Permission granted to photocopy for personal use only.

The Magic Chest

Whenever the lil' Wizards enter the basement and find the magic chest, they discover that it has a unique locking mechanism. There's no keyhole but instead the lock is centered on a circular hole about three inches wide. It looks like something can be placed inside.

If the Wizards have already collected all the fragments and put them together, it's instantly obvious that the medallion fits into the hole. If they've found at least two pieces (thus giving them an idea of the medallion's rough size and shape), an observant character notices the same thing. Any player who asks point blank whether the medallion probably fits in the hole should be told that yes, it probably will.

Once the medallion is inserted, it starts spinning quickly in the lock. If Mr. Filmon is in the room he jumps toward the chest, shouting "Nooooooo!" and tries to remove the medallion (if he isn't, he enters just as the medallion starts spinning, with the same result).

It is, however, impossible to remove the medallion. The chest vibrates more and more until the lid finally pops open and a burst of light floods out, momentarily blinding everyone in the room. When their vision clears, they see the Squeakydoor ghost floating above the open chest. He stretches and waves, greeting them in a child's voice: "Hi! Thanks for letting me out of there! Do you want to play with me?"

If the Wizards ask how the ghost got into the chest, Mr. Filmon confesses...

Read to the Players

"It was me. I locked him in the chest because he was scaring away all the hotel guests."

Mr. Filmon looks at the ghost, ashamed. "I shouldn't have done that to you. I'm sorry."

The ghost smiles, and hovers over close to Mr. Filmon. "It's all right. I know I can be scary sometimes... But most of the people I've met like to be scared! When I used to live here, everyone really loved it."

Mr. Filmon blinks, surprised. "You lived here?"

At this point the ghost tells the story about his family building the manor, and him getting lost in the woods while hiding to scare his sister (*see page 117 for all the details*). He's really impressed (and touched) if the lil' Wizards already know any of the story, which they may have learned from the books in the library or from Captain Graybeard.

Mr. Filmon is embarrassed and begs the ghost's forgiveness. Fortunately, the ghost is more than happy to give it, especially since the hotel owner spent so much time reading to him, and thus the Tale concludes.

There's still the question of how the lil' Wizards get home, and whether they help Mr. Filmon and the hotel guests realize their dreams and put on a stage show, but those don't have to happen unless you want. For now, the mystery is solved, the ghost is free, and everyone can enjoy the rest of their stay at the Squeakydoor Manor!

Epilogue

After the chest is opened, Mr. Filmon is happy to give the ghost a chance. The hotel owner needs help with all his work and the ghost could lend a hand in the kitchen or the laundry, or even at the front desk. Maybe the ghost could perform a haunting show, and there's no better storyteller than a ghost when it comes to the spooky stories that Shiverers love so much.

If the lil' Wizards learned that some or all of the guests have music in common, and especially if they made the connection that each guest can help with a stage show, they could convince everyone to pitch in and put something together. Any of the following might happen...

+ Miss Hasbin could set her musical in the hotel and rename it the "Squeakydoor Musical Spooktacular!"

+ The wood shed could be replaced with an outdoor stage. The inner courtyard's acoustics are amazing!

+ In addition to building the stage, Mac Piston could erect sets and rig up some lights.

+ Pumpkin Jack could paint the sets and stage props.

+ Captain Graybeard could entertain audiences with colorful curses and high seas stories between acts.

+ Count Gregory could manage the show and arrange for a steady stream of ticket buyers.

+ The ghost could finally get to perform on stage.

+ Mr. Filmon may realize his dream of putting on the plays of The Bard.

Even if none of this happens the lil' Wizards still have many more stories ahead of them. After a good night's sleep (or three), Mr. Filmon bids them farewell but makes sure they know they're welcome back anytime.

What's the next Tale? That's up to you! The whole of Coinworld awaits, and in a place like this almost anything could happen...

Hand out any remaining Lil' Points, and include some extra if the Wizards helped with the stage show.

The Journey Home

Eventually the lil' Wizards find their way home. Perhaps Gideon Herasmus catches up with them, wanting to know about the manor mystery. Maybe they find a Weird Object that takes them back to Heads. They might stay on Tails for a while, visiting Bones or Screams, or somewhere else. Only one thing is certain: for the lil' Wizards, every day is a new adventure.

THE END...

...or maybe not!

Home Archipelago : ....

Name : ....

Player : ....

Traits

Body ....

Heart ....

Brain ....

Powers

Common

Broom Riding ....

Spellcasting ....

Sorcerer

Alchemy ....

Divination ....

Mage

Conjuring ....

Shapechanging ....

Skills

....

....

....

Description

Appearance
....
....

Signature Features
....
....

Personality
....
....

Tastes
....
....

Motivations
....
....

Background
....
....

Belongings

....

Wizard Gear

Broom ....

Wand ....

Hat ....

Familiar ....

Lil' Points